BEYOND THE EGG TIMER

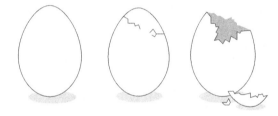

*A Companion Guide for Having Babies
in Your Mid-Thirties and Older*

Sharon Praissman Fisher
& Emma Williams

LYSTRA BOOKS
& Literary Services

This book is for inspirational and motivational purposes only. Please discuss your medical and mental health issues with a qualified professional.

Beyond the Egg Timer: A Companion Guide for Having Babies in Your Mid-Thirties and Older
Copyright © Sharon Praissman Fisher and Emma Williams, 2018

ISBN, print 978-0-9991958-7-1

ISBN, ebook 978-0-9991958-8-8

Library of Congress Control Number 2018936390

LYSTRA BOOKS
& Literary Services

Published by Lystra Books & Literary Services, LLC
391 Lystra Estates Drive, Chapel Hill, NC 27517
lystrabooks@gmail.com

Authors' photo by Mark Poole

Cover design by Silke Stein

Interior book design by Kelly Prelipp Lojk

For you dear reader.
This is the book we wanted you to have
and we needed to write.

Contents

Foreword

By Jodilyn Owen, LM,CPM

As I write this I have just completed a clinic day—sitting for hours in the company of women who are engaged in the profound work of womanhood. That is to say, they are struggling with learning to create meaning from events in their lives that are hard on the heart and seeking to understand who and how they will be as parents in the near future. They each have their own journey into pregnancy, yet they all share the work of growing a baby while gearing up for parenthood within the complex social, political, and cultural layers of their lives.

As a midwife, I spend an hour or more at each prenatal visit. Over the course of this hour I hear the stories of the families I serve—their fears and longings, expectations and hopes, past hurts in the healthcare system, and intentions for their pregnancy and birth. I am treated to a glimpse of the path that brought these families to my door. As the years of conversations accumulate, I have learned to recognize the patterns, process, and progression of these conversations. I am gifted with a profession that trained me to listen, and not to lecture. When we create space for feeling heard, felt, and understood in healthcare, the patient becomes a partner and a leader, showing us when and which skills to use for her benefit. When we look a patient in the eye and tell her, "You will be OK, this will change and lift and get better. You can do this and I will be with you," we are a platform for people to reach their own potential. I like to think that midwifery care is the confluence of love, justice, and healthcare. It is certainly the lens I have come to see my work through.

Sharon and Emma have created a holding space where we can finally discuss and dig into the pursuit of parenthood after the age of 35 from this model. They have found a way to share what they've learned, to bring to the front the words and experiences of women just like you who have worried, struggled, and tried to find their way through the maze of daunting fertility options. They demonstrate on page after page that the only truth that matters is that you will find what is right for you, even when it does not line up with what is right for others or fall in line with what one might call "normal." As I read their work, I am reminded of all the women who sat on the couch in our clinic and cried because they were labeled "high risk" or of "advanced maternal age" and given stern warnings about genetic anomalies and the hardships of raising children after they had "passed their prime." It is hard enough to conceive, but they move right from joy over the positive pregnancy test to absolute terror. This book changes that narrative. What comes with this journey is certainly trial, error, retrial, adjustments, pain, love, humor, and lots of hormones. But your strength and abilities also come roaring along and will carry you through.

Here is the truth: I have met many women in the past ten years who are over 35 who are healthy, vibrant, energized by their lives, and ready to parent. They often present in better physical health, with fewer underlying conditions, than women in their twenties. When and how we choose to birth and parent has become a social justice issue on many fronts. But for this work, we can focus on the rights of women to self-actualize. For many of us this means finishing college or developing a career or traveling or (don't be scared) getting to know ourselves or heal ourselves from painful experiences before we look for a partner or consider having children. For many, the idea of growing up together in a partnership is unappealing—we want to find mature and established people to date, partner, and parent with. Many women want to parent without a second parent. This is life! We are full of diversity *and* possibility. Whether or not our biology wants to come along for the ride can come into question when trying to conceive into our mid-thirties and beyond. This book helps illuminate the importance of the process of becoming a parent as one of coming further into oneself, of growth, of grief, of healing.

Women over 35 who are investigating the possibility of parenthood tend to be business owners, high-level executives, or accomplished professionals. Now is not the time to relinquish the skills you have developed that have helped you achieve these successes. It is a time to leverage them to help you learn, move through a system, ask a lot of questions, and find providers you trust to partner with you. At the same time, pregnancy and birth are where we are primed to let go of our chronos-bound ideas: all the charts and graphs, expectations for performance and assessments of efficiency and production. In trying to conceive, you will both call on the skills that you have from your life thus far and embrace the feeling of letting everything go and accepting the moments you find yourself in. This is no small task. *Beyond the Egg Timer* offers suggestions and creative solutions for existing in this *time-bound* and *time-out-of-time* experience. It is yours to take the suggestions and mold them into workable and meaningful practices for you.

I often wonder about the science of epigenetics and today's "older" mothers. We know that environment, mental health, behaviors, and exposure to the myriad of external and internal influences in our lives change how our DNA expresses itself. Studies of separated twins and twins at different ages have shown that nature does not trump nurture. Indeed, nature needs nurture to reach its potential. How we treat ourselves—emotionally and physically—can suppress or bring forth our biological reality. We are resilient overall and can heal from difficult childhood experiences, disease, or trauma in our adult lives. Modern medicine is looking at how to use epigenetic triggers to reverse disease and improve immune response.

You will find in the pages of this book multiple references to the important influence you can have over your reproductive health through nutrition, rest, stress-recovery tools, and adjunctive therapies that all nourish the body and soul. By the time you are 30 you have probably found what gives you joy in your life and what gives you energy. Move into those activities as you navigate this process. You don't have to be the perfect patient and parent—you just have to be perfect at being you and remain open to the possibilities that each day might bring.

You don't have to be the perfect patient and parent—you just have to be perfect at being you and remain open to the possibilities that each day might bring.

Two hundred years ago women had a life expectancy of 40 years. At the age of 40 today, most of us are just hitting our stride and gearing up to take on the world! Our bodies are strong and most of us reading this book will have access to nutrition, shelter, and opportunities for education and growth. All of these factors lend to the ways our bodies function. And sometimes, we do everything we can and we are not able to realize our goals. Through months and years of trying to conceive or conceiving and experiencing pregnancy loss, we cannot know all of the whys, either positive or negative. The stories in this book, along with Sharon and Emma's evaluation and suggestions, demonstrate that finding the goodness in our lives separate from conception is paramount to your mental health on this journey. Be kind to yourself, and take heart that your truth will rise and you will recognize it when it does.

There are women who will read this book as they explore their interest in childbearing and decide not to become parents. There are women who will read this book and try absolutely everything and be unable to conceive. I want to be sure that you are recognized. I want to tell you what is very rarely said out loud to women at any point in our lives, and especially to those who cannot or choose not to have children. Your value is not reduced to the few square inches where your uterus resides. Your uterus is not society's commodity to value or devalue as the politics may dictate. Your value is the creative energy you put into the world, the way you walk through your life and create meaning in each day for yourself and those you encounter along the way. The link between the health, education, and success of women to the health, education, and success of all of society is clear. With or without children, our value is realized when we find a place to pour our creative energy that generates feelings of wholeness and satisfaction within. Let this book be one step in the process of actualizing your deepest self and fulfilling your potential as a human.

I will leave you with parting words borrowed from a dear client who came to me at the age of 40. After over a dozen years of trying to conceive, she sat across from me in my office and introduced her children, ages 2, 3, and 5. She explained that she had a 14-year-old who was in school. None of them were her biological children; they all found their way to her through family members who could not care for them or through her church. She looked me straight in the eye and said, "I have come to understand through my life as a barren woman that we do not know how we are to be made mothers in this world. I own my own business and I nourish that and fret over it like a newborn. I have a brother who could not care for his children and here they are, with me until he can bring them home. They call me mama. I was nearby when a distraught teen faced a foster system that would let him down. I create art using a medium that I love to explore. My creative self, my uterus, my heart, my mind have manifested in all these ways and more, and I have a great peace about the events in my life. I am not barren, I am replete with nutrients that grow these surprising and fulfilling sprouts."

She thought she had hit menopause but had, in fact, conceived. She went on to have an incredibly joyful and healthy pregnancy, though it was remarkable for the emotional retooling she did to see herself as a biological mother and to understand what that might mean in her life. Her baby's birth was one of the most profound I have ever attended. She knew herself and understood her place in this world and would not allow the idea of a biologically childless life prevent her from manifesting her creativity or playing a deeply important role in the lives of children, something that she valued deeply.

My wish for all of us is that we find peace where we are, clear sight for where we want to be, and a lovely road map to guide us as we close the gap between these two places. I think you will find, as I did, that *Beyond the Egg Timer* will provide you with the tools to realize this in your own life and to help provide some practical wisdom, excellent role models, and comfort along the way.

Introduction

If you are in your thirties or older and are thinking about when or whether or how to become a mother, you may feel overwhelmed by options and choices. We would love to have written a book that would give you a special formula for making a baby in a way that feels right to you. The truth is, no one can do that. However, this book is meant to help ease the stress and tension that sometimes accompany conception by giving you accurate information and new ways to respond to your situation and navigate the journey.

This is the book for those of you who have been trying to conceive for a while and those of you who woke up yesterday and realized you forgot to have a baby. It is for those of you who had difficulty finding the right partner, were unsure if you wanted children until now, are part of the roughly 10 percent of the population who experiences infertility, or delayed motherhood because it did not seem financially practical. In short, we wrote this book in hopes of helping women who vary a lot in circumstances but are similar in that they are childless and are still hoping to become a mother, or at least considering it.

We also wrote *Beyond the Egg Timer* because we needed it. While celebrating Emma's fortieth birthday over a delicious Italian dinner, she mused that it would be great if there was a book with accurate, supportive information for women having babies later in life. The next day, Sharon called her to propose writing one. Our personal experiences, professional background, and deep desire to help other women drove us to explore this topic. We did this by collecting real women's personal stories, reviewing scientific research, and developing evidence-based advice you might need if you are experiencing the same kinds of challenges. As we learned more, we saw common themes emerge. *Beyond the Egg Timer* is divided into three sections to reflect three reasons women are having babies later in life: indecision, infertility, and, simply, the way life happens.

We also want to counter the notion that any one solution will work for all women. We have benefited from reading other women's memoirs on the subject, but we all live our own unique story. Each section includes first-person stories from real (anonymous) women who had their children after age 35, followed by our reflection on the story, based on our research and experience. By sharing stories from other women in similar circumstances, we seek to widen readers' perspectives. We also offer two types of advice interspersed throughout the book:

1. **Coping techniques**, for stress management during this time. The coping techniques offered work best when practiced repeatedly over time. They will create a space in your mind that is clear and calm, and that space will become your safe harbor.

2. **Pregtiquette**, a term we coined to refer to the social awkwardness that can arise around trying to conceive and being pregnant.

If you have delayed childbearing because of indecision, the first section may appeal to you. This section reviews some challenges around contemporary American motherhood and includes three women's stories that embody these challenges. Many women experience ambivalence around whether to have children or not. We discuss how to address uncertainty on the part of you or your spouse (or both), and how to respond to intrusive questions about your intentions to have children. Even if you feel completely certain that you want to be a mother, this section may help you think through common concerns around relationship, career, and finances.

Section 2 gives real information about how likely you are to get pregnant naturally (spoiler alert: very likely!) and what to do if you haven't conceived within six to twelve months. The narratives reflect different fertility issues and approaches to resolving them. We also talk about miscarriage, the role of stress in fertility, and some coping techniques.

The last section presents some more ideas for managing stress—in which we will NOT tell you to "just relax." We discuss timing of sex, which can be a cause of anxiety and strain marital relationships. We also share three stories from some seriously wise and insightful women.

We also share our own stories throughout this book. We know intimately the experience of having children later in life and have faced our own challenges. We both experienced highs and lows in the journey and sought information wherever we could.

After reading the book, we hope you will have found your own magic formula to overcome indecision (if you have any), cope with fertility issues (if you have any), and find the time that feels right for you.

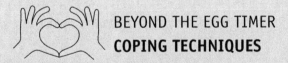

BEYOND THE EGG TIMER
COPING TECHNIQUES

#1 Connect With Others, Chapter 4

#2 Enjoying Life in the Meantime, Chapter 7

#3 Maintaining Flexibility and Humor, Chapter 8

#4 Navigating Your Course, Chapter 8

#5 Mindfulness, Chapter 9

#6 Cognitive Behavior Therapy, Chapter 10

#7 Protecting Yourself, Chapter 12

#8 Acceptance, Chapter 13

SECTION 1

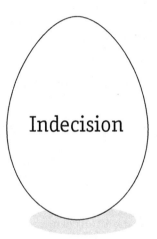

Indecision

1 How Did We Get Here?

As we mentioned in the introduction, we wrote this book because we needed it. When we decided to write it, Sharon was newly married, trying to get pregnant, and finding that it presented a depressing array of physical and emotional challenges. Meanwhile, in the space of three years, Emma had gone from fearing that she would never conceive to mothering a baby, a toddler, and a puppy. So, Sharon needed to write the book as a coping strategy, Emma needed to write it to figure out what the hell just happened to her life, and we both yearned to provide a resource and some comfort to women in similar circumstances. We started talking to women with interesting stories to share, and they recommended other women for us to interview. Sharon adapted the most valuable insights she had learned as a psychiatric nurse practitioner and a Buddhist lay teacher to make them applicable to women on the path to motherhood. To find further insights, we both delved into relevant social science and medical research.

We thought our book would take about six months to write. It has taken almost five years. Planning to write your first book in six months is probably as unrealistic as thinking you are infertile if you do not get pregnant within six months of trying to conceive. This is but one of the many things we have learned on this journey, things we want to share with you.

Since this is a book of sharing stories, and we want to let you know that we are fellow travelers on this journey, we'll start by sharing our stories.

Emma's Story

My experience of trying to get pregnant was fairly mundane and yet utterly life-changing. When I was in my twenties, I joked that if we had more women in medical research, there would be a test you could take when you were 22 that would predict your fertility for the next fifteen to twenty years. Doctors would put a blood sample into a computer, and a little slip of paper, like the ones inside a fortune cookie, would pop out with a prognosis. Yours might say, "You have a good chance of conceiving a baby within the next five years. After that, not so much." Your friend's might say, "If you miss your pill even once before the age of 45, you will get pregnant. Be careful." Your sister's might say, "Get a second job, and save that money for in vitro fertilization (IVF)."

Wouldn't it be great if we knew early on how soon we should begin trying to conceive? To know when making a baby should be at the top of our priority list? When we talked, almost all of my friends wanted to have children, but just not then. And yet, we would hear stories from older friends and cousins that would make us nervous about waiting too long.

As it turned out, the time never felt right until a few years after I married at age 32. I suddenly yearned for a baby, and my husband did too. At the same time, my career felt unsettled. After finding my work as a medical researcher unsatisfying, I briefly started training for another career, but then that felt wrong, and I went back to my old job. Then, at age 34, I found out I was pregnant. Suddenly, everything seemed to make sense, and I had a project on which to focus my energy. All was well until I went for a sixteen-week ultrasound, hoping to find out the baby's gender, and instead found out that there was no fetal heartbeat. The grief I felt was nearly devastating.

Once again, it was an opportunity to ponder the mysteries of fertility. I have known so many women who were trying to have children and inexplicably had problems. I have friends who hadn't eaten junk food since the 1980s and who had tried everything from acupuncture to IVF. They'd had procedures, talked to experts, and they still didn't get pregnant. Meanwhile, in the city where I live, there's a special obstetric clinic for pregnant women who are addicted to drugs. I don't know what those women eat, but it is unlikely to be an organic diet based on the principles of Chinese medicine, and yet the clinic is always full.

When I think back to my imaginary fertility predictor, it was based on the faulty assumption that fertility is static or predictable throughout one's life. Actually, a lot of evidence suggests the contrary, such as my own experience. Fertility is unpredictable, and that makes it fascinating to me.

As I alluded to at the beginning of this chapter, everything worked out for me in the end—even better than I had hoped. I will tell you the rest of the story in Chapter 5.

Sharon's Story

I've always wanted to be a mom. At various points in my life, I have also wanted to be an Olympic luger, veterinarian, wildlife biologist, lawyer, nurse, nonprofit organizer, motivational speaker, wife, professional sailor, and farmer. I have actually been some of these things. The one constant, however, was that I always wanted to be a mom. Growing up, I was the neighborhood babysitter and always volunteered to hold or help with any baby around. I stayed with friends and relatives after they birthed to help with the wee one (or two)! I rejoiced in their joy and patiently anticipated my turn.

I did everything in the "correct" order: went to college, traveled, started a career (wildlife biologist), went back to college and started a new career (nurse), bought a house, figured out who I was so I could meet the best partner for me, got married, and tried to start a family.

I was 34 when we started and had enough humility to understand it wouldn't happen right away. My husband and I both come from families with fertility issues and assumed we would have some problems. However, I never imagined I would still be on this journey years later. As each friend and colleague announced their pregnancy, I was positive I would at least be pregnant by the time they gave birth. I had helped others with their babies for decades; surely my day would come soon.

I started using the fertility awareness method (FAM) (more on that in Chapters 7, 11, and Recommended Resources Section), then I went for acupuncture treatments, which left me feeling great and got me ovulating regularly. After about eighteen months—including some time off from trying because of post-graduate training—I went to a reproductive endocrinologist for evaluation.

A hysterosalpingogram (HSG) test (which is an X-ray of the reproductive tract) found a giant polyp that was taking up too much real estate in my uterus. The doctor felt that the polyp was the culprit, scheduled surgery a few months later, and afterwards told me to come back in three months if I wasn't pregnant. She explained the three-month deadline was based on my age and how long we had been trying. If we got to that point, she would start me on Clomid, a fertility drug that causes you to release more eggs.

With each month's period, I would get the blues, but overall, I was fairly optimistic. It still hadn't been two years, and we had found a reason to explain the infertility. I also had learned a lot about my body and had improved my health with a better diet. The downside was I had become obsessive about timing intercourse correctly. This put some strain on our marriage, but we managed the stress with constant communication.

I didn't get pregnant or expect much that summer. I was under a lot of stress and often had a physical reaction to that. We also missed an entire cycle helping a friend move his boat in the Caribbean. (Tough life, I know.) I did not start Clomid at the three-month check-up, still feeling that things would happen naturally. My husband was against it, as well.

September marked the two-year anniversary of when we started trying to conceive and that month's negative pregnancy test was particularly devastating. In my mind, I had created a scenario in which I would magically get pregnant when it was the "right" time. I, in my arrogance, thought I knew when that would be. I also had the mistaken belief that because I had always been a caretaker professionally and personally, that I was somehow "owed" a baby. My best friend once referred to me as Mother Earth. It seemed unimaginable that I wouldn't be a mother.

Maybe you're like me: ambitious, goal-oriented, and experienced at working really hard and really smart toward something and achieving it. I give a lot, expect a lot, and, at the core, attempt to control a lot. But here is the thing: pregnancy is not like that. Parenting is certainly not like that. Life is not like that. You can't control it, nor can you control the outcome.

I know the lessons I've learned from this journey will make me a better mother eventually. If it had been easy, I would have been the kind of mother who expects my child to get into Harvard because I fed him organic food and read to him every night. Instead, I will make extra effort to delight in my child for all that he or she is.

It has already made me a better wife. I used to envy the women whose husbands were baby crazy. Now, I am so grateful my husband is the steady, rational support. It has made me more compassionate; very few people know my pain, since I typically look positive and strong. Now I have a clearer appreciation of everyone else's inner battle. It has made me know my strength and the strength of my marriage. My journey has deepened my faith, which has been my lighthouse, guiding me safely home from some dark places. Those are some of my whys. They evolve daily and make the journey so worthwhile.

I will share the rest of my story in Chapter 6 and in the Epilogue.

As you reflect on our stories, and the stories to come, you'll see similar themes emerge and that the women we interviewed struggled with multiple issues. You'll also see that many of us didn't know a lot about how to navigate the path to motherhood, either psychologically or medically. Meanwhile, we received lots of messages suggesting that we had put ourselves—and maybe even our potential babies—at risk by waiting until our thirties or forties to try to conceive.

Then again, for many of us, having babies at this age seems like the new normal. That's because age at first birth is strongly dependent on where you live and how well educated you are, with urban and well-educated women being more likely to delay motherhood. But just because everyone is doing it does not mean that everyone is talking about it. Fertility challenges are still a fairly taboo subject in our society, with many women and couples keeping their experiences to themselves. On the other hand, as some women interviewed for the book described, women also often scare other women with dramatic stories about fertility challenges or nightmarish birth scenarios. Even though many women share our journey, it can still feel like a lonely journey at the time.

The overriding goal of this book is to normalize having children later in life. Although we clarify statistics and offer a more accurate view of fertility (in Section 2), it does not mean your fertility stays intact forever. There is an end point. Our message here is not that you should immediately start trying to conceive or book an appointment with a fertility specialist. We want to give you new ways of thinking about things. Our aim in sharing other women's insights is simply to present different perspectives to give you a better chance at understanding your own feelings and concerns.

Choice Fatigue
In the next section, we talk about various sources of uncertainty, which include ambivalence about motherhood, concerns

about how to balance career and family, decisions about marriage and relationships, and figuring out how to pay for all the costs related to pregnancy and children. In this context of uncertainty, we may also have choice fatigue. For many, all choices are possible. Have children in partnership without getting married. Get married without having children. Be a single parent. Or even choose not to parent. A desire to choose the most right, authentic, satisfying path can lead to indecision. Psychologist Barry Schwartz has written a book about this called *The Paradox of Choice: Why More is Less*. His take is that the problem with having so many choices is that it can lead to "paralysis rather than liberation." One reason this could occur is that we have heightened awareness of what we may have lost by not having made a different choice. Another reason is that we may have higher expectations of the results after having made a choice, which could lead to regret if things turn out differently than expected.[1]

It may feel like the optimal choice is impossible. For most of us, there's never really a great time to take a six-week unpaid maternity leave.

Like Sharon said, growing up, many of us were advised to focus on our careers first, then have children. When this choice comes with fertility challenges, or still makes it seem impossible to balance career and baby, we may feel outraged that we made the "right" choice, yet it did not work out for the best. It may feel like the optimal choice is impossible. For most of us, there's never really a great time to take a six-week unpaid maternity leave.

Of course, we are not saying that having so many choices is negative on the whole, or that it would be better to go back to the good old days when, as Schwartz says, the only choice was who you married, "not the when or what you did after [marriage]." (Often, the "who" had not even been within the bride's purview.)

We think all of this uncertainty is completely understandable.

We continue this discussion throughout the book, but here is the important thing: the right time is when you say it is. Wait until you have found the right partner—or don't. Wait until you've reached a certain level of career attainment—or trust that it will all work out. Perhaps you will decide that motherhood is not for you. But if you do decide it is right, our hope for you is that you will find the right time and, in retrospect, it will seem that things worked out with the best possible timing.

2 The Realist

S ome of life's great delights come from making a bold change, even though it is impossible to know how things will turn out. Choosing motherhood requires a special boldness, because it cannot be undone. You can divorce the spouse, drop out of the university, quit the job, and grow back the hair, but motherhood is different. You cannot put the baby back—and hardly anyone would want to, because they are very cute.

Some women are unsure if they ever want to become a mother. Full stop. This leads to questions about what motherhood entails and what it looks like. This ambivalence may stem from social pressure, a relationship (or the absence of it), and many other sources.

Some women want motherhood only after specific circumstances have been met, such as marriage and financial security. Without those conditions, they are faced with tough decisions. Amidst these concerns are whether you can really trust yourself to make the right choice about having a baby, especially if you are living with regrets because of your past decisions. Put another way, if your life is going well, then do you really want to change it? If it is not going well, then why add more stress? We can also feel opposing social pressures from family, colleagues, friends, and romantic partners. Women have to sort through all these conflicting thoughts and feelings, while facing tremendous pressure to feel relentlessly joyful in the face of a dramatic and uncertain life change.

In this chapter, you meet Erin, an ambitious and happily married woman who struggled to decide if becoming a mother was the right choice for her. Her story exemplifies many of the themes discussed in this section of the book on indecision: marriage breakup, lack of societal support for working mothers, questions about being maternal enough, ageism—and even climate change. Although those are pretty serious subjects, Erin had us laughing out loud about them.

Ultimately, her experience begs the question: What if your response to uncertainty is to just let things happen?

Erin's Story

Throughout my whole life, I never really had that affinity for babies and children, which contributed to my waiting to have a baby. An aunt or a grandma at one point said to me, "Never trust a man who doesn't like children, dogs, and old people." And I remember saying, "Hmm, well, I don't really like any of those things either, so maybe we'd get along fine."

I divorced when I was about 28, and I started dating Ron not too long afterwards. We dated on and off for a year, then we lived together for four years before we got married.

I tell people, jokingly, we got married for financial reasons. I was a faculty member, and if we married he could take a freelance but higher paying job and be on my health insurance.

We had talked a lot about having kids, just bouncing it around, even prior to getting married. I had always thought I would have kids, mainly because it's what people do. That's the expectation: everyone has kids.

I always considered it an option, but was not set on the idea. My husband loves kids, but had no strong opinion about having his own either. At the time, we already had ten nieces and nephews, so we thought we could enjoy the child-free life while still having children in our lives.

PREGTIQUETTE

How to Handle Intrusive Questions About Having Children

We can never truly know someone else's motivation. However, it can be helpful to speculate on why people ask whether you have children. In some circles, it's considered part of polite conversation. The motivation is benign, and it is no different than asking someone about their job. Nonetheless, if you are feeling uncertain about whether

You may feel like providing some explanation for your lack of children. However, a simple "no" suffices.

you want to become a mother or if you are trying to conceive and feeling upset about how long it is taking, the question may make you feel sad, defensive, or irritated. You may feel like providing some explanation for your lack of children, either because of defensive emotions or from a desire to share your frustration. However, a simple "no" suffices and will prevent anyone from feeling uncomfortable. No is a complete sentence.

Most of the time this works and the conversation shifts to another topic. However, not everyone gets the hint. Some people will persist in questioning you about when you will have children or why you don't have any yet.

Ultimately, the antidote for these scenarios is unapologetic confidence. Have confidence in your ability to one day become a parent as well as with the decisions you are making along the way. Have confidence in your ability to shut down the conversation before it makes you uncomfortable.

Most importantly, have confidence in your overall self and life. (You will use this confidence again later when people forcefully expound their ideas of how you should parent and whether you should have a second child.)

The following vignette demonstrates our point. Picture Sheila with a confident, indulgent smile and a calm demeanor throughout the entire conversation.

Aunt Mary: "So when are you going to make your mom a grandmother?"

Sheila: "Oh, hopefully sooner than later."

Aunt Mary: "Well, you should get on it! No one's getting younger here!"

Sheila: "We are waiting until the time is right. What's new with you?"

Aunt Mary persists...

Aunt Mary: "You know, Debbie down at my office did IVF and got a great set of twins! You should just do that if you don't get pregnant soon!"

Sheila: "Thanks, Aunt Mary, but we got it under control, and it's not up for discussion. How are you and Uncle Henry doing?"

Sheila was able to handle Aunt Mary by maintaining a neutral, kind, and firm stance. That is what confidence looks like. She did not get defensive. She made no direct response to the comment about aging. She tried to redirect the conversation subtly, and when that did not work she took a firm stance. Gaining confidence takes some work, but it is a skill that can be learned through practice.

We had all kinds of reasons on both sides of the argument. Knowing that women on average live longer than men, I had a fear of being old and alone. So I would say to my husband, "You know you're going to die before me, and I'll be completely by myself."

On the other hand, there were practical things we considered. I'm not much of an environmentalist, but one of my reasons was that the Earth is overpopulated. With seven billion people on the planet, why should I have another one? We seem to be sucking the life out of our planet. Why reproduce?

Financially, I didn't think I would be able to be a stay-at-home mom. I was worried about balancing it all. I was the oldest of three children, and I felt that I had seen all of the work that it entails. I tend to be a realist. My roommate in college said I was a pessimist. And I would say, "You're an idealist, and I'm a realist. That's the difference."

So we laughed and jokingly came up with all sorts of reasons, but at the heart of it was that we had a very nice life the way it was. Then again, I didn't want to be one of those crotchety old people who don't have kids, and I wanted to experience pregnancy.

I was in a doctoral program until May 2010, and it did not seem practical to have children before then. When I graduated, I was 36. We decided that I would go off the birth control pill and let fate decide. For the next four months, I was in a state of panic that I would get pregnant. Part of the problem was that it was just so strange to try to get pregnant, after trying to prevent pregnancy for so many years. I felt that my anxiety was a sign that I was not ready to have a baby. I went back on the birth control pill, but I did a really bad job of it. I remember, once, my mom giving advice to someone who was trying to get pregnant. She said something like, "Buy a car that you can barely afford. You'll get pregnant. That's how life works." Well, not really trying to follow her advice, we bought a boat. Every decent boat has a big cooler, and a lot of beer. I conceived on July 4, 2011 somewhere in the middle of a river.

My pregnancy was normal. My ob-gyn wrote AMA on my ultrasound paper in the medical conditions category. I looked endlessly at it, trying to figure out what it meant. Did they misprint someone else's disease on my chart? I couldn't think of any medical condition that they would think I might have. I tried all combinations of nonsensical medical words to figure out what disease this poor person had that they accidentally wrote on my order form. Adult myelocytic anemia? Acute myopic angular? Angular myasthenia association? Abdominal mesenteric artery? Acetabular muscular aneurysm?

Then, I thought, "Great, I bet it means against medical advice, which means I am going to have to pay for this blasted ultrasound, because someone thinks this twelve-week ultrasound screening is unnecessary." Then I thought "No, no, that can't be. This is standard care for people my age, since I am a geriatric primigravida!" Just then it dawned on me. "AMA is an abbreviation for advanced maternal age... They called me OLD."

UNEXPECTED BLESSINGS

As I said, I never had an affinity toward children, but once I had my daughter, it was like a whole other world. I just feel completely different about her, and I never would have expected that. Until you've had a child of your own, you just don't know. Knowing what we know now, about how great it's been to have her, about how much we laughed, and how she's brought us closer together, I probably would have done it sooner.

Many things are hard in relation to time and scheduling, and in our own personal time together. Clearly, your sex life takes a dip when there's a nineteen-month-old lying in between you. But I look at my husband differently because I see how much he loves her. I just see him as more of a nurturing, loving person, and we have a connection that's very different now. And I think he feels the same way about me. So, I think it's something that's actually been great for our marriage. Now we have a very common goal and a common purpose.

Every now and then we'll lie in bed at night and look at each other and say, like, "Hey, we've got a kid, did you know that? There's a kid in that other room, and she belongs to us. Is that weird or what? But she's ours. Like, half your genes and half my genes, and she's sleeping in that room over there." We have a little symbol that we have used for her since I was pregnant. We point a middle finger down to the ground and twirl it like a tornado or Tasmanian devil. That was how we fondly envisioned her, spinning around our house leaving a trail of mayhem. Whenever one of us thought, "OMG, we are going to have a kid," or "OMG, we have a kid," we would do the universal symbol and smile at each other in disbelief. It's been such a great thing that I often tear up at the thought that we almost didn't have her in our life.

Although it's hard, it's not as hard as I made it out to be. I think you just reprioritize your life. You do have to make room, but you just tick things off. Things become less important to you. My house was in perfect order all the time before she came, and it's not so much anymore, but it's OK. It doesn't bother me as much as I thought it would. You just change your priorities. It's hard working full-time, rushing out of work to try to get home, dealing with traffic, and the whole time thinking, "I'm going to be late I'm going to be late I'm going to be late." But then there she is, and she comes running at me, and it's all worth it.

It doesn't have to be hard. It doesn't have to be hard on your marriage and all of those things. I think it's actually kind of fun. We love to travel, and we thought with kids it would be impossible, but we just plan our trips with her in mind. We can wait to go to Alaska until she's older, but in the meantime, we can go to visit that crazy mouse and the princesses. Surprisingly, those places are so much fun for us too—nothing like watching magic through the eyes of a child.

When I had her, I was 38, and now at 39 we wonder if we should have two. I think we've pretty much decided we're just going to have her. Often when people asked me if I'm going to have another child, I tell them what an angel my daughter is. I believe that nothing in life is free and that what seems too good to be true probably is. Because of that, I am acutely aware that the universe is likely playing a trick on me. Something like, "We will give her a really good first child and trick her into having a second one." I have never been a gambling person because I am too logical. There is just no way that I would get a kid this good twice!

Our Reflection on Erin's Story

Once, we asked our friend Hannah Caradonna,* a therapist and mom living in British Columbia, to write a guest post for our *Beyond the Egg Timer* blog on *Psychology Today*, because we knew she would have great insights. The title of the post was: "I Don't Want to Have Children if It Changes My Life Too Much." She wrote:

I remember, at the end of my first pregnancy, feeling like I had been packing for and anticipating a vacation, yet I had no idea where I was going or exactly when it was going to happen. I didn't know what to pack and didn't even know what questions to ask to prepare for my voyage.

A baby shifts everything. Here is what it is like: You are balancing these different aspects of life carefully. Then, your baby is born and the birth throws everything off of the scale, and all that is left is the baby. All the pieces fall back onto the scale slowly, over the course of weeks/months/years, but their

---

*Hannah Caradonna is a psychotherapist, mother, and old knitting buddy of ours who currently lives and works in Victoria, British Columbia. You can learn more about her at www.victoriapsychotherapy.com.

weight changes. And here's the kicker: you don't really know which items will maintain the same weight and which will carry less. But, the sum total of time you have in one day stays the same. This means that you have time to do everything you like, but some things will be done less frequently.

This also means that your attitude toward work will shift so dramatically that it may not be worth putting too much thought into this before the baby comes. You may continue on the same career path after having a baby or go in a completely different direction, but it is not something that can be known until after it happens.

In addition to Erin's concern about how a baby would affect her and her husband's relationship, she also alluded to a concern that she might not be innately maternal enough. Maternal ambivalence is a taboo subject, certainly not something mothers will casually chat about at preschool story time. Yet in her study of maternal ambivalence titled *The Monster Within: The Hidden Side of Motherhood,* psychiatrist Dr. Barbara Almond called it a "ubiquitous" emotion. Dr. Almond wrote, "I believe that today's expectations for good mothering have become so hard to live with, the standards so draconian, that maternal ambivalence has increased and at the same time become more unacceptable to society as a whole." She described a spectrum of maternal ambivalence from "good-enough mothering" that involves some degree of ambivalence to more extreme fears of having a monstrous baby, passing her own faults on to her child, being unable to love her baby, and having a baby who is unable to love her. It's possible to feel reluctance and longing at the same time.

Our purpose here is not to persuade readers to hold fast to the child-free lifestyle. Despite all these drawbacks and concerns that Erin described, she and many of our friends and other women interviewed for this project have told us that becoming a parent was actually more satisfying than they expected. One shocking bit of wisdom Emma received during her first pregnancy was that having a baby would actually make her *more* efficient. This seemed to contradict other experiences that women had shared about how babies left them chronically sleep deprived or resulted in them requiring two hours to leave the house before a short trip to the grocery store. But now she has lived this paradox of both compromised and enhanced efficiency. Lisa Solomon, an artist and professor, described this phenomenon once on Tiffany Han's podcast.[2] Solomon said, "Having a kid ... completely changes your universe, and what you can do definitely changes, especially in the beginning ... The first two or three years are so challenging, in terms of figuring out how to keep doing what you love doing and not feel guilty and not feel like you're overcompensating and not feel like you're messing up in some areas of life."

Then Han said, "Balance is bullshit." (That would make a great conversation starter t-shirt to wear to play dates, until your children learn to read!)

Solomon said, "It may look like I'm balanced, but ... there are twenty million balls in the air, and I just catch the one that's going to fall and break. I can catch it and throw it back up in the air. And then I wait for the next one that's going to break. And I catch it." Later she said, "I used to be like, 'I need eight hours in the studio if I'm really going to get anything done 'cause I need to look at something and I have to listen to the right music.' And now [after having a child] it's like, 'Half an hour? What can I get done?'"

WRAP: A Helpful Device for Making Up Your Mind

In their book *Decisive*, Chip and Dan Heath offer a framework for decision making[3] based on the acronym WRAP, which can also be applied to fertility decisions.

W. First, **widen** your options. So often, we get caught up in dichotomous thinking, "or" instead of "and." If you have been avoiding a fertility clinic because you absolutely know you don't want to do an intrauterine insemination (IUI) or in vitro fertilization (IVF), this is "or" thinking. Go and get an evaluation. Perhaps the issue is fibroids, which can be removed, or your husband has a low sperm count, which can be improved with nutrition. Sharon and her husband benefited from using both Eastern and Western medical approaches to conceiving. They started with FAM, which showed that Sharon ovulated irregularly. She then made dietary changes based on Chinese medicine and had acupuncture. This got her ovulating regularly but not pregnant. They then got evaluated at a fertility clinic and learned that Sharon had a giant uterine polyp. Her doctor thought this benign growth might be preventing implantation of an embryo, so surgery was scheduled to remove it. Afterwards, they continued using FAM to time intercourse during the most fertile window.

R. Second, **reality-test** your assumptions. Erin never really had an affinity toward children, but that all changed once her daughter was born. Erin said, "Until you have a child of your own, you just don't know. Knowing what we know about how great it is to have her [...] and how she's brought us together, I probably would have done it [embrace motherhood] sooner."

Erin was also concerned about her age. Too many women are under the assumption that age 35 is a "fertility cliff" when that is simply not true.

A. Third, **attain distance** before deciding. There is nothing more fraught with emotions than issues concerning our children (conceived or not). It may help to take a step back before making big decisions and really consider how your choices align with your core values. This can be harder if you are constantly being told that time is running out. In reality, taking an extra month for reflection will not matter in the long run. Like many of the other couples featured in this book, Erin and her husband took time in deciding their course of action and ultimately conceived.

P. Lastly, **prepare to be wrong.** This one is a lot more optimistic than it sounds. The idea is to be open-minded when finding a solution, because we never truly know how things will turn out. K.K. Goldberg, author of the memoir *The Doctor and The Stork,* started with a fierce resistance to Western medical intervention, but after three years of trying to conceive she and her husband finally chose in vitro fertilization (IVF). Later, Sharon interviewed her and she said, "I wish I had done it after six months of TTC [trying to conceive]! I would counsel my younger self to get right to it. However, I had a profound phobia about doctors and medicine that's hard to describe to others who don't share it. I know my younger self would have rejected this advice—I

certainly had the intellectual capacity to recognize this
option. For me, in hindsight, the emotional stress of failing
to conceive was far greater than the hardships of IVF. The
hard part of IVF was waiting at the end, and the notion of
spending so much money and emotion for possibly negative
results. Everyone comes to the next right choice in their
own way and time. Going forward, though, I have a strong
idea that it's best to go right to the big move! Invest in
possibility. My future self is more open to this."

3 The House Hunt

In this chapter we meet Charlotte, who met her husband, Sam, when she was in her mid-thirties and knew pretty soon that he was the right guy. But the right house, the right job, and the right time to start a family seemed frustratingly elusive. Meanwhile, she worried that they were waiting too long to have children. This narrative addresses the question: What happens when a desire for motherhood seems hopelessly blocked by circumstances?

As a young adult, Charlotte had not contemplated motherhood seriously. Working as a nanny had given her an up-close view of how difficult it is to combine a career and motherhood. Like Erin (the realist), she felt either pessimistic or realistic, depending on whom you ask, about climate change and other global challenges and about the realities of parenthood in the United States.

Charlotte's Story

My husband and I met on the commuter train. We spent six months riding the train together every morning before he finally asked me out. I was about 34 years old then, training for my black belt in hapkido, and eating a mostly paleo diet. I was thin and fit and had tons of energy. Despite its slow start, the relationship moved really quickly. I felt a strong nesting instinct and a desire to have kids with him.

Sam wanted to move in after a couple of months of dating, but that was too fast for me. He felt strongly about living together for a year before getting married. In other ways, he wanted to pretend that the relationship was not serious, even though it was. He had just finished his PhD, and this was his first job in his chosen career. He had that college-student mentality and lifestyle longer than a lot of people do. He was ambivalent about becoming a father for years.

Ultimately, we moved in together and married several years later, when I was 38. During that time, Sam remained reluctant about having children. There were several times when I said, "I want to let you know that by not trying to conceive, we might actually be making the decision to not have kids. If we delay too long, it won't be possible." However, he never really thought my age was a concern.

Things changed for Sam after his best friend from high school started to have kids—after being married for almost 20 years! I think it's because the husband finally got tenure; before that, academics have to work long hours for a relatively low salary. So, Sam started to think we should have kids. I think he finally gave himself permission to be somebody who could be a father.

[Once Sam was on board, both Charlotte and Sam became concerned that their lifestyle was not right for a baby.]

When we got married, we rented this little shack of a house while waiting for real estate prices to become more affordable. Sam did not want to have kids until we were settled in our home, but that kept getting put off because of the housing bubble. We finally started looking at the beginning of 2009 and didn't move until September 1 of that year. At that time, the swine flu was in full swing and it seemed that pregnant women were being affected more intensely, so we continued to feel that it was the wrong time to get pregnant. (In retrospect, that doesn't seem like a serious concern.)

My career had changed to the point where I didn't have time to work out, because I was working sixty to seventy hours per week, putting in a lot of late nights, and had a long commute.

Around that time we started house hunting. I quit my stressful full-time job, partly because we wanted to start a family eventually and it was my first step to make room for that. (That said, I was working so many hours with so little reward that even if we never had kids I knew I wanted to make a change.) I had to relax and heal all of that. We can heal, but it just takes time, and not everybody has that time.

TEST STRIPS AND SPREADSHEETS

So, we put off actively trying to get pregnant until I was 41. I started with ovulation test strips but later realized I was using them at the wrong time of my cycle. In December of that year, I read Taking Charge of Your Fertility by Toni Weschler and started charting my menstrual cycles consistently, using a spreadsheet. Although I knew nothing was certain, I expected to get pregnant within several cycles since I knew I was still ovulating. Through charting, I determined that my luteal phase (post ovulatory) was fairly short, just at the low end of normal.

After we started trying, I worked to clean up my diet and lifestyle, eating only organic foods, limiting carbohydrate consumption, and eliminating all refined carbohydrates. I created a spreadsheet to track my diet and make sure I was getting all the recommended daily allowances of essential nutrients. My routine included weight training and walking. Over nine months, I ended up losing about sixty-five pounds and felt that I somewhat normalized my endocrine system. For example, my luteal phase became a day or two longer.

Although Sam started out ambivalent, by the time we began trying to conceive, our anticipation, excitement, and intermittent ambivalence had become about equal. Overall, trying to conceive was a fun and renewing project for us, which brought us closer.

I was a good five to ten years behind friends and relatives in my general age group who wanted kids, including my sister *who had two children. We also had some friends who chose not to have kids, and for years we had fallen into that group of couples without kids. It was part of our identity, kind of, not having kids. We really didn't discuss the process of trying to conceive with anyone we knew, except one close friend, because we felt that it was a very private decision and process.*

[Charlotte never considered medical intervention to improve her fertility; she said it's not her style. They looked into adoption, but were told that it would be difficult for a couple in their forties.]

So, we continued trying. I tried a few things to boost my chances of conceiving. The first was making homemade kefir, to add more probiotics to my diet. That helped

It was part of our identity, kind of, not having kids.

with a few lingering digestive issues I was having. The other detail is that for that one cycle, I decided to try doing the yoga bridge pose right after sex.[4] I just remember thinking "what the hell" because I really was about to quit trying. Because of charting, I knew I had had a couple of very early miscarriages. Although I never had a positive pregnancy test, I had high temperatures, suggesting the hormones were kicking in. They may have been bad eggs. That's the thing about being our age: you just have to hit the right egg.

It took me eighteen cycles to conceive. I knew after about a week, and it was more like waiting for my period. I didn't feel pregnant until after about eight weeks. And I delivered a healthy baby at age 44.

In retrospect, the one thing I would definitely do differently is to try to conceive much earlier, as soon as we got married. It seems now like a bad decision to have delayed pregnancy until we had bought our house. We could have functioned in the space we had with a small baby. Also, I wonder if pregnancy, delivery, and the postpartum period would have been easier if I had been five years younger. You're never going to have a perfect situation. I believe there was a lot of luck involved in our ability to conceive. It could have gone the other way, and we took a huge chance by waiting so long.

Our Reflection on Charlotte's Story

It is often the case that we have an idea of what we want motherhood to look like, and our reality seems so different. Bridging that distance can feel impossible. Then odd circumstances, like the swine-flu panic mentioned in this story, spring up and further conflict with the vision we have for pregnancy. Charlotte also expressed a situation we have heard from friends and women interviewed for this book: sometimes one spouse feels uncertain, sometimes both feel uncertain, and often both experience changes in heart over time. We have two ideas to help couples in this situation that we present here. The first is using the speaker-listener technique, and the second is widening the conversation.

The Speaker-Listener Technique

We know women, ourselves included, who delayed motherhood because they wanted to wait and find the right partner. But what if you have a great partner, and you have decided you want to become a mother, but your partner is unsure or thinks you have all of the time in the world? First, try to understand the source of hesitation. Is it financial concerns, parenting skills, or the vague but prevalent "not feeling ready"?

Whatever the source of concern, dedicate time to really understand your partner's views. One time-tested approach is the "speaker-listener technique"[5] in which one partner speaks about his or her perspective on a subject. Then the other tries to summarize what the partner just said. Then the first person responds to whether the summary reflected what they meant to say. Although it may feel frustrating, the objective is not to impart your view, it is to understand your partner's. For this to work, you must adopt that mindset. As an example, here's an imagined version of Charlotte and Sam talking about his reluctance around fatherhood, in the phase before his friend became a father and his feelings shifted. Sam is in the role of speaker, and Charlotte is in the role of listener.

Sam: I just don't feel ready to become a father. I just finished being a doctoral student, working so hard for a small stipend. Now I finally have a decent salary, and I want to enjoy life.

Charlotte: You are worried that we don't have enough money to support a child and that we will have to be really frugal like when you were in grad school.

Sam: That's part of it, but I think we probably do have enough money. It's more that I just finished this huge responsibility of finishing my doctorate, and I don't want to take on another huge burden.

Charlotte: You just finished with one huge responsibility and are unsure about taking on another? Fatherhood feels overwhelming to you, in some ways, and you are not sure you want to take that on yet?

The thing to note here is that Charlotte simply tried to get to the heart of Sam's reluctance, without expressing her own views, even though she was probably freaking out inside hearing him describe fatherhood as a burden. The goal of this exercise is to develop compassion and understanding for your partner's view. It is not to express your own opinions or desires. There is a time and place for that, but not when you are trying to understand your spouse's reluctance at that moment. Views change over time, sometimes dramatically—that's a theme from Charlotte's life and several other stories in this book.

(By the way, Charlotte's husband loves being a dad now.)

Widening the Conversation

Psychotherapist Hannah Caradonna wrote on our blog, "Understanding each other's dreams and fears are a huge part of being able to negotiate parenting and your relationship. Ultimately, every couple has to find their own way through the shift in becoming parents. I recommend starting the conversation early and keeping it going throughout the various stages of parenthood. You and your spouse are the foundation of your family, and that is what will carry you through this journey."[6]

Caradonna created a list of questions to start the conversation about parenting:

1. What gives you deep and great joy now?
2. What do you hope for and why?
3. What are your favorite memories from your childhood?
4. What are your least favorite memories?
5. What were your parents' roles at home growing up?
6. What aspects of your mother and father's parenting practices do you hope to carry on as a parent?
7. What aspects of your mother and father's parenting do you hope to do differently?
8. What do you want for your children in life?
9. Describe the ideal parent in your opinion and why.
10. Thinking about friends and family who have children, who do you feel can be a role model for you and why?
11. What do you think you would most enjoy about being a parent?
12. What do you think would be the most difficult part of being a parent?
13. What are some things that you would like to do now that would seem to be more difficult as a parent?
14. What do you do now that you might have to sacrifice to be parents? In other words, how will the child change your life, career, finances, lifestyle?

Ten Minutes, Ten Days, Ten Years

In the last chapter, we described the WRAP technique for making decisions. Another ambivalence-resolving technique that is suggested by Chip and Dan Heath is thinking of yourself ten minutes, ten days, and ten years out from your decision. With the decision about whether to have children, as we discussed, one source of anxiety is that you have no idea what your life will look like ten years from now. That is OK, but allow yourself to dream about what you would want your life to look like. Again, if you start to think that your life with children will not include certain things, reality-test those assumptions. People travel with children; they build careers while parenting. Heck, Emma and Sharon wrote a book while parenting and having careers! If you start to think that you must have certain things (such as a certain house) before starting a family, reflect on whether that is absolutely necessary.

Both Erin and Charlotte were contemplating motherhood in the context of marriage. However, many women in their thirties and forties actually feel certain that they would like to become mothers—if they could find the right partner. Their challenge is that they have not found the right partner yet and wonder if it is wise to delay childbearing until marriage. In the next chapter, we talk about a woman who faced that challenge and decided to become a single mother by choice.

4   Smart Enough

This is a story about deciding what course is right for you and following it, regardless of social expectations—and then laughing about it years later. Nicole was in her thirties and living in San Francisco when she suddenly decided she was ready to have a baby. As a child, she had only thought about motherhood in terms of wishing she could have had a mother more typical in appearance and behavior than her own Bohemian artist mother. In her twenties, she had felt ambivalent about motherhood, as she performed as a dancer and came out as a lesbian. Then things shifted and she started to feel a pull toward motherhood.

Nicole's Story

I started thinking I want the experience of being pregnant and giving birth. I want to know what this is like, because this seems like a really interesting deal, and not everyone can do it, and you kind of want to not miss out.

The real clincher for me was when I befriended a fellow Pilates teacher who was in her fifties and single. One time she told me, "I always wanted a partner first. Now, I'm in my fifties, and I'm alone. I don't have a partner, and I don't have a child." After that conversation, I decided that I needed to do it.

At the time, I was in a relationship with a woman. We were supposed to get married, and I wanted to have a baby. She didn't really want to. Her attitude was that she would be a good parent, but it would be because I wanted it. It would be by default for her, like the cat she inherited from a former girlfriend.

Still, we would chat about it, and one time she got excited about asking this one guy for sperm.

And then I asked him, and he said no. And then we broke up. I spent a year after we broke up being miserable, and then I started trying to get pregnant.

Before I started trying, I went to a doctor to get checked out to make sure I was all right. I didn't have a regular doctor, so I went to someone I'd never seen before. She did a pelvic exam, and she said, "Your pelvis is great. You've got a lot of room in there."

(I did have a really easy birth.)

Then she sat me down, and she was like, "You are going into this by yourself. Can you really afford this?" Although she was right, I felt like it wasn't really her place to be asking me that. I just felt really bad and irresponsible, like I was being scolded, and it put me on the defensive.

Then I told my friend Jane, who is an artist and married to an artist, about this experience. She was outraged that the doctor would say such a thing. She said, "You know, we're a married couple. No one's going to ask us, 'Can we afford this?' No, we can't afford it. We're both artists, but we're going to do it anyway. But because we're married, we're not getting that kind of doubt and judgment."

I started going to meetings of a group called Single Mothers by Choice. The other members were all upper middle class straight women who owned homes in expensive neighborhoods and drove nice cars. They were all anxiety-ridden and asking themselves if they could do it alone. I had a really cavalier attitude. I was like, "Look you guys, if I can do it, and I'm poor, you can do it."

(But I didn't know what I was getting into. At all.)

MOURNING

For them, there were a few stages of mourning. The first stage of mourning was that they didn't have a husband. They had always dreamed of being married and having a child, and now they were going to have to deal with not having this male presence. For me, that was no big deal. I already knew I was going to have a donor, because I'd been with women for so long, and I never planned on being with men again. So, the donor part was a given. But for them it was very saddening. And then, some of them tried with a donor, couldn't get pregnant, and were told that biologically they were unlikely to conceive. So then they were trying to adopt and were grieving that they couldn't give birth.

I was really naïve about the whole thing. And like everything I do, I didn't research anything. I read books about childbirth, but I didn't read a single book about parenting. I had no idea what I was doing.

I think that was partly because of how I was raised. In my family, you got knocked up by accident, and then it was a big drag. My mother's four children were born over a twenty-year span, clearly unplanned. She had her first baby at 19 with a guy who was an alcoholic artist, and they weren't married. It was shameful in those days, and she got fired from her job because she was pregnant. She left him because he drank too much and later married my father. When I was older, I saw my older brother dating single mothers, and he liked it. He thought women with children were attractive and great. So for me, there wasn't this convention of it having to be a certain way.

The other thing was, I didn't have money, but I thought, "Whatever. People go on welfare all the time. If it gets that bad, I could go on welfare. If I get in trouble, I could move in with my parents."

(I did end up moving back in with them at one point, and it was horrible.)

When I was in my twenties, I knew this band who traveled all over Eastern Europe in a van with their two kids. I thought, "What is the big deal? They can do it. Why are these parents *going on so much about how hard it is and how they don't get any sleep or don't get to do the things they used to? What a bunch of whiners."*

(Now, of course, I realize that I owe them all an apology.)

THE SEARCH FOR A DONOR

I started asking men I knew if they would be my sperm donor. It was not that awkward, because they all knew I was trying to get pregnant. Plus, they all knew I was gay. It was San Francisco, so it wasn't like the craziest thing they had ever heard. They were all flattered.

[The first potential donor declined because his father had abandoned him as a young child and being a donor felt like abandonment to him. Another potential donor said yes, but his wife, who was also Nicole's friend, said no way. The wife was older, didn't want children, and was afraid that the experience might make her husband want children that she would be unable and unwilling to provide. The next man she asked said no, because he wanted to find someone and marry her and have babies. Another friend volunteered, but he had a history of drug addiction and depression, which made Nicole say no. She asked her downstairs neighbor, since he had red hair like her, and he said no. One of Nicole's friends tried to recruit a German guy who was visiting San Francisco, but he already had a kid with someone he wasn't married to and found the situation really difficult. Nicole gave him a fairy doll with blue skin to take home to his little girl. After that, she gave up on finding someone she knew and tried the sperm bank. More hilarity ensued.]

Ever since I got my period, my cycle was irregular, anywhere from twenty days to forty-seven days. When you're using frozen sperm, you have to know when you're ovulating because it doesn't stay viable very long. It was also incredibly expensive.

They would take one ejaculate and split it into five or ten units. Each unit would come in a tiny pink vial the size of the tip of your pinkie. One time the sperm was packaged in a huge metal tank that looked like a cross between an old-fashioned milk jug and a fire extinguisher. The tank was knee high, and I had to carry it home on the train. People stared at me. All of the paint was eaten off of it, so it looked like some vintage bomb.

But it didn't work.

Another time, I brought an insulated lunch bag, and they packed it full of dry ice and put the sample in there. This time, there was dry ice smoke coming out of the zipper when I was on the train.

After a few tries, I gave up on that because I couldn't afford it.

One day my younger sister emailed me and said, "For whatever it's worth, I know someone who's willing to donate. He'll make a cute baby, and he won't try to take over." (This is an issue you hear about all the time: the donor sues for custody. In California, it doesn't matter what kind of verbal or written agreement you have, if you know your donor, the court always rules in favor of the child. The child deserves two parents, so the donor always wins joint custody.)

My sister had been friends with him as a child. He's eleven or twelve years younger than me, so at the time I was 36 and he was 25. I emailed him and asked, "Why do you want to do this?" Because what kind of person does that? Total egomaniac, right? My friends who said no, they had humility. They had a sense of responsibility. They felt that conceiving a child would be precious to them.

When he wrote back, he said the subject came up when he and my sister were talking about their sisters wanting to get pregnant. His sister was trying to conceive and was unsuccessful and very unhappy. So, he was happy to help me. Also, he knew and liked my family. And he said it's important for children to have as much family as possible and as many people who love them as possible.

[Fortunately, he was also living nearby in Berkeley. Nicole met him for the first time at his house. In his front yard, there was a fig tree covered in fruit. It seemed like a good omen of fertility. When Nicole peeked through his window, she thought he was cute.]

He was prepared to show me stuff about his family or his medical records. I asked him if he had any addictions or depression in his family, because my family is riddled with that. And he said no. I didn't care if the donor was smart, because I'm smart enough. I wanted him to be happy. That was all. So, we decided to try.

Since I was monitoring my cycle, typically I would call him up and say, "I need to try today." He would come to my house, I would give him a jar, and then I would leave my house, because I felt like it would be too weird if I was in the other room. So I would take a walk, and he would call me when he was done. Then I would meet him on the stairs, and I would say, "Bye." And he would say, "Bye." Then I would go to my room, suck up the sperm with a syringe, put it inside myself, and lie there with my butt up on pillows.

One time it was Thanksgiving weekend and it was time to try, but when I called him he didn't call me back right away, like he usually did. I got really upset about it. I was in Al-Anon at the time, so I would call other Al-Anon members when I was upset. So I called my cussing hardass friend Jackie. She said, "Listen, you have anxiety, and even if he was there, giving you his sperm, you would still have anxiety. Because anxiety is free floating, and it will attach itself to anything you're thinking about."

Eventually, he did call me, and I got some, and that time it worked. It was nine months before my daughter's birthday.

There are a lot of people who say that becoming a single mother is really irresponsible. It cheats the child. It's completely selfish. You know what? It probably is all those things. I didn't think about what it would be like for my daughter to grow up with just me. I didn't think about how I could afford it. I didn't think about how hard it would be for me. I don't regret doing it at all, and I don't think that I should have been forbidden from doing it.

How many straight people are getting knocked up by accident? I had to work for this.

Then again, I think straight people need to think about it too. How many straight people are getting knocked up by accident? I had to work for this.

What do people think is so great about marriage? I certainly never had a good impression of it. My father worked his ass off, and he was reliable about going to work. But he was angry about it, because my mother never worked, and we were always poor. My parents fought all the time, and they literally threw things at each other. One time my mother slammed the door over and over until the wood split. I used to beg them to get divorced.

THE REALITY OF MOTHERHOOD

My baby was one of those babies who cries all the time, except when she was eating or sleeping. Friends that I had expected to help me were unavailable, although other people I knew less well helped a lot. It was overwhelming, but I know most new mothers feel overwhelmed whether or not they have a partner. Also, I had postpartum depression. When my baby was eight months old, I moved cross-country to live with my parents, partly because I needed help and partly because my father was diagnosed with cancer.

It was awful living in that house again, because of the memories it brought up. But my parents loved having us there. Every night, my father and my daughter would touch their foreheads together to say goodnight. Before he died, he wrote me a note that said, "You and she are the one bright light."

After that, I stayed in the same city, bought my own house, and went back to school to get a master's degree. I'm not dating anyone now, although admittedly I haven't tried that hard. I feel isolated at times. It seems like everyone is straight and married. The only single mothers I meet are devastated because they're going through divorce. Or they got knocked up and don't appreciate how lucky they are, since I worked my ass off to get pregnant.

My daughter's father also moved back to the East Coast and sees her several times a year. She is still his only child. When I was finishing my master's thesis, he came and helped take care of her for an entire week. I feel good about where my daughter and I are in our lives now. We have lots of friends to support us, my career is going well, and home life is more stable and nurturing than mine was as a child.

Our Reflection on Nicole's Story

Over the past seventy years or so in the United States, raising children outside of marriage has shifted from a shamed and stigmatized behavior to a widely acceptable practice. Based on 2011–2013 data collected by the Centers for Disease Control, 78 percent of women and 69 percent of men agreed with the statement, "It is OK for an unmarried female to have and raise a child." Although births to unmarried women declined slightly in recent years, still 40 percent of births in the United States were to unmarried women. Among women ages 35–39, 22 percent of mothers were unmarried, and among women ages 40 and older, 24 percent of mothers were unmarried.[7] Of course, many of these women had a partner who was not their legal spouse, but the point is that getting pregnant while unmarried no longer requires you to move to Switzerland, telling everyone you are just going to study French with your spinster aunt (like in the show *Downton Abbey*). Deciding whether that choice makes sense for you personally is a subject that merits its own book. Yet some concerns are similar for all women, regardless of whether they have a partner, such as finances and career.

Can I Afford to Have a Child?

Nicole felt confident about her ability to support a child on her own, but other people, such as the doctor she described, tried to discourage her based partly on financial reasons. She also met other women who seemed more well off than she was, yet faced doubts about their own ability to provide financially for a child. Many couples delay childbearing for financial concerns.

In addition to the fact that women earn less than men on average, the "motherhood gap" in wages has been well documented, with moms earning less than childless women over the course of a lifetime. However, on average, older moms are at a financial advantage compared to younger women. This is not surprising given that people earn more on average the longer they have spent in the workforce. Like Sharon and some of the other women who have shared their stories in this book, many women delay childbearing because they are getting an advanced degree, which could also lead to a higher salary. Some evidence even suggests that the motherhood gap may not exist for women who wait until at least age 31 to have their first child.[8]

The cost of childcare is another daunting prospect for those considering motherhood. Between 1985 and 2011, the average weekly cost of childcare rose 70 percent, from $84 to $143 with adjustments for inflation, according to U.S. census data.[9] These figures included childcare provided by family members. Of course, families with one child paid less on average ($114) than families with two children or more ($164–$169). Also, costs were much higher if the family's youngest child was less than five years old ($179) than if the child is 5–14 years old ($93). (After having children in East Coast cities, these national averages sound pretty low to us.)

Affordability of childcare varied by income level; families living in poverty paid about 30 percent of their income for childcare, while for others the average was 8 percent. Between 1997 and 2011, the percentage of working mothers who paid for childcare declined from 42 percent to 32 percent. Nonetheless, 61 percent of preschoolers and 50 percent of grade school children were in some form of childcare in 2011. None of these figures address the quality concerns or what many parents experience as a struggle to find good quality care that is conveniently located and is a good fit for their child.

All of this is to say that if you have delayed motherhood because you are worried it will have a negative impact financially, in terms of wages and cost of childcare, we understand that, and the data suggest that you are right. Although it is a bit beyond the scope of this work, we believe that the U.S. society can, and should, do far more to protect children from living in poverty. On the other hand, people at all income levels have children, and we are also subject to external pressures or beliefs about scarcity that are exaggerated. For example, it was inspiring to read about Emma's friend's relatives, who were featured in a *Washington Post* article because they have thirteen children and live debt free on one income.[10]

In *The Soul of Money*, Lynne Twist and Teresa Baker write about sufficiency as the opposite of scarcity. "We each have the choice in any setting to step back and let go of the mindset of scarcity," they write. They explain, "Sufficiency...is an experience, a context we generate, a declaration, a knowing that there is enough, and that we are enough."[11] They suggest that focusing attention on what we have rather than what we do not have is one pathway to greater joy.

In *Saved*, Ben Hewitt explores how we find the boundary between scarcity and sufficiency. "We need money, we think," he wrote. "We need this and we need that. We must accumulate these things so that someday we can exist free of the need to accumulate these things. So that someday, we can occupy our lives to the extent we know is possible but cannot afford just yet. I probably do not need to point out that this is a trap."[12] But Hewitt's example would be hard for most people to follow: he and his wife constructed their own off-the-grid house in rural Vermont and grow most of their own food.

Now, if you want to drop everything and go live off the grid in Vermont, we will cheer you on. We also understand if you are living a more typical American existence—mortgage or rent, plus lots of monthly expenses, including food—and cannot clearly see how you could either (a) do without you or your partner's income altogether (if you have a partner) or (b) find an extra $114–$169 per week for childcare. We see both sides of this dilemma. It is a reasonable concern, but it can also become an endless concern, because in some ways no amount of money is ever seen as enough in mainstream American culture.

How a Baby Will Affect Your Career

So many books, blog posts, movies, novels, television shows, and magazine articles have explored the tension between women and careers that it is hard to know where to begin. In the United States, having a baby often means paying hefty medical fees and taking unpaid maternity leave, if you are even eligible for maternity leave. Surely you have heard of the pay gap and career disadvantages faced by women who are mothers.

And then there's how the baby will affect your career. In America, many of us are taught to equate career with self-identity and even self-worth. Ann-Marie Slaughter's 2012 article in *The Atlantic* "Why Women Still Can't Have It All" summarized the challenges many women face. A professor at Princeton, Slaughter writes that she had once thought it possible to balance career and motherhood. Then, taking a high-profile government job with long hours and a rigid work schedule made her rethink things. Slaughter writes, "I still strongly believe that women can 'have it all' (and that men can too). I believe that we can 'have it all at the same time.' But not today, not with the way America's economy and society are currently structured."[13] She cites some practical examples, such as the difference between school schedules and work schedules, policies against offsite work, as well as some emotional differences, such as women being more likely to feel guilty for spending less time with children.

She also writes about this big myth: sequencing things correctly can make it easier. Based on the personal challenges she experienced when conceiving, she recommends trying to have a baby before age 35 or "freezing your eggs." (We do not necessarily agree with that suggestion. See Chapter 5, "Fertile Enough.")

These are big issues and we don't presume to have the answers for them. We do know that sharing with others normalizes the situation so you don't feel so isolated and overwhelmed with juggling it all (or deciding if you really want to even try). Below is a coping technique that is critical for every stage of the journey.

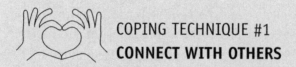

COPING TECHNIQUE #1
CONNECT WITH OTHERS

Nicole describes seeking support from her friends, her sister, the Single Mothers by Choice group (singlemothersbychoice. org), and Al-Anon. Before that, it was through conversation that she realized that she wanted to become a mother before finding a partner. Sharing her thoughts with her sister led to her connecting with her sperm donor. Human beings are social animals, and we need each other. Before, during, and after you try to conceive, build a support network for yourself, either in person or online or both.

The advantage of support groups, whether in-person or online, is that they normalize your situation. Seeing others facing the same obstacles will remind you that you are not alone, nor is your situation unique. If it is not unique, then there must be hope. Group members may offer insights that can help you. They include a mix of women at different points in the journey. You will learn from others as you are able to support and inspire each other. These groups are also a safe harbor to express the range of emotions (some not so pretty) that accompany this journey.

Support from friends or family can be helpful, if you can recruit those who will respect your privacy, offer non-judgmental support, listen without advising, and take cues from you. You may have to guide others on how to help you, as loved ones are not mind readers. It's helpful to have several support people, as different people offer different viewpoints and styles of support. However, it can be preferable to choose people who aren't overly emotionally invested in your fertility, or at least proceed with extreme caution when relying on your parents and siblings. Friends in your age group can become pregnant or wish they were in a position to try to conceive, so be thoughtful about that as well. If you participate in a faith community, your religious leader and members of the congregation may be supportive and offer comforting guidance. In addition, some of us benefit from professional counseling during this time.

PREGTIQUETTE

Responding to Someone Else's Pregnancy Announcement

Sometimes, you may feel joy if you hear a certain friend is pregnant. Other times, you may be overcome with jealousy when a different friend announces her pregnancy. It's not at all logical. It may not even be indicative of how you actually feel about the friend. Please know that it is normal, though. Because you can't control when and how others will announce their pregnancy, it is helpful to have some planned responses. Below are some types of announcements:

Announcement Type 1: *Your cousin Lauren announces at the Thanksgiving table that she is pregnant with baby no. 3 and giggles, "We just look at each other, and I get pregnant."*

Response Option 1 & Only: The only reasonable response is to smile and congratulate her. Any other public reaction will not change the fact that she is pregnant, and you are not. If you feel tears approaching, tell yourself that babies happen and that you could be next. Think about something funny. Whatever it takes, be gracious. You can have a good long hard cry later on. Also, keep perspective. Maybe she does get pregnant easily, but what comes easily to you that may be emotionally challenging to her? Are you naturally thin? Are you always popular in any crowd? Was school easy for you? These things may not seem comparable, but everything is perspective.

Announcement Type 2: *Your good friend sends you an email announcing that she is pregnant and she hopes the news doesn't upset you too much since she knows that you have been trying to conceive.*

Check in with yourself and how you are feeling. Your friend clearly meant well. Maybe you are feeling upbeat, and her pregnancy feels like evidence that you too will get pregnant soon. Then again, maybe the part about it not upsetting you strikes you as presumptive and condescending. If you feel upset, walk away for twenty-four hours. The beauty of the email notification is that you don't have to respond immediately.

Response Option 1: Email, or even call, and congratulate her. Ask her about due date, how she is feeling, etc. Don't mention anything about yourself or your fertility journey. After all, it is her moment. Yours will come too.

Response Option 2: Do as above and add that you appreciate her thoughts and concern about you, but not to worry. Tell her you are confident you will be pregnant soon.

In short, whether or not you have a baby in the context of a committed relationship, expect that you will need emotional support and discern what kind of support would be most beneficial. At the same time, expect that not all advice will be helpful and supportive, like the doctor who tried to give Nicole a reality check about motherhood but just made her feel bad. Ultimately, it is likely that your choices will make some people unhappy, and that is part of life.

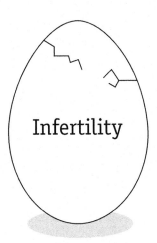

Infertility

5 Fertile Enough

As we described in Chapter 1, Sharon tried to conceive for more than one year before a reproductive endocrinologist discovered a polyp that may have been preventing conception. After the surgery to remove it, her doctor told her to come back in three months if she wasn't pregnant yet. Sharon would then be prescribed Clomid, a medicine that makes you produce more eggs. She explained the three-month deadline was based on Sharon's age and how long they had been trying. Sharon and her husband waited a few months longer because of circumstances and a belief that things would happen naturally.

Sharon's Story

September marked the two-year anniversary of when we started trying to conceive. That month's negative pregnancy test was particularly devastating. That fall, we tried Clomid. My periods were light when I was on it, which made me question how it was affecting my uterine lining. Plus, although there are no studies to support its affect on mood, I felt more depressed on it. We then switched to Femara, another medication that improves ovulation regularity. I was on that for about eight months, meanwhile continuing with acupuncture and dietary changes based on Chinese medicine. We did an intrauterine insemination (IUI) sometime in that period without success. It was disappointing to say the least.

The Femara did not seem to have any side effects, but wasn't helping either, so I asked the doctor to increase the dose. She was skeptical that it would help but agreed to try. The cycle be-fore the second IUI, the ultrasound showed a lot of eggs form-ing. My doctor said that if I were a younger woman they would cancel the cycle rather than create the next octo-mom (not ac-tually her words). In the end, only three eggs fully formed, and we all agreed it was worth the risk. I secretly wanted twins but knew triplets would be too much for us.

Around this time, I learned about the "law of attraction" as described in Rhonda Byrne's audio books The Secret *and* The Power. *Listening to her voice and conviction were captivating and made my forty-five-minute commute sail. According to Byrne, the law of attraction is based on love. Generate as much love as you can and truly believe you are living the life you want. Picture what you want and picture the life you want to create as if you already have it.*

At first, I was doubtful but decided to try it. I was delayed getting home one night, because I was picking up a restaurant gift card for a friend's birthday present. I thought about how good a friend he had been to me and generated love for him and his wife. I pictured them enjoying the dinner they would get with the gift card. I then decided to try to manifest something for myself.

Byrne suggests you start with something small, so I chose a chocolate chip cookie. I pictured the cookie. I imagined what it would smell like and how it would taste. I did this mentally until I could feel how it would taste in my mouth. When I got home, my husband had a cookie waiting for me! This had never happened before. They had a free lunch at work and through a series of cookie swaps everyone got the kind they wanted, and there was even an extra one, which my husband, Bryan, brought home for me. After that experience, I was hooked.

To be consistent with this approach, I decided to step down from moderating a peer-support group organized by RESOLVE: The National Infertility Organization. The group had been essential for my sanity at one point, but I no longer felt I needed it. Following Byrne's law of attraction, I wanted to define myself as fertile. I even got some friends into it, and they would say things like, "No, you can't go to the beach this year, you'll be too pregnant and uncomfortable!" or "Stop! That's raw cheese. You can't eat it while pregnant!"

I also tried to generate as much love as I could. Even when I was having a bad day, I would make lists of things that I loved. I would include everything from how the sun felt on my face to my cat to running water. I would also picture myself pregnant or with a small baby.

The fertility center sent me for a pregnancy blood test a couple weeks later. I worked for the same health center, so could access all of my records. Before looking at the computer screen, I generated as much love as I could. I created the possibility that I was pregnant. When I opened my eyes, I saw I was pregnant. I just started crying. I then desperately needed to tell someone. I wanted to tell my husband in person so I did the next logical thing: I texted Emma about a million times. She was in a meeting and couldn't respond. I then called my good friend, Nina, who worked down the hall from me and had been a huge source of support, but she was occupied with an emergency patient. So in the end, I went home and told my husband first, as it should be.

He was stunned.

My husband always points out that we had sex the night before the IUI, so we're not really sure if the procedure worked or if we conceived naturally.

At four weeks, we went in for the first ultrasound and saw one beautiful gestational sac with a fetal pole. Over the next nine months, she grew into a spectacular baby girl.

Sometimes I think about how our lives would be different if we had conceived right away. Would I appreciate it as much? Would I parent differently? It's easy to say now that I wouldn't *have wanted it to turn out any differently. That is a luxury I have, now that everything has worked out.*

The Truth About Fertility

When we titled this section "Infertility," we meant that a bit ironically. Current research suggests that less than 1 percent of couples are truly infertile. However, in common medical practice, if you are over 35 and have been trying to conceive for six months without success, you may be labeled as infertile. The media, coupled with popular misconceptions, can exaggerate the risks of trying to conceive over 35. Take comfort, as you will read below, your chances of having a healthy baby are quite high.

Approximately 60 percent of couples between ages 35 and 39 will conceive within six months of trying. By the one-year mark, 82 percent of those couples will achieve pregnancy.[14] After two years, 90 percent of couples will conceive on their own. This is great news if you are in the 90 percent. What about the other 10 percent? According to a German study, another 5 percent will conceive within thirty-six months of trying.[15] That leaves only 5 percent without a baby after three years of trying. The authors felt that it was doubtful that those couples would ever conceive unassisted. However, a British study found that only 1 percent of the population trying to conceive truly is sterile, meaning they could never have a child without intervention, although probability declines with age.[16] Most older couples can conceive naturally, but not necessarily quickly.

If the overwhelming majority of us can get pregnant on our own, why do we know so many couples undergoing fertility treatments?

If the overwhelming majority of us can get pregnant on our own, why do we know so many couples undergoing fertility treatments? The answers are varied and complicated. Many couples are not willing to wait the full two years, particularly couples who want more than one child and feel that time is running out. Some people believe, if the technology exists, they might as well take advantage of it. For others, their patience wears out before their eggs and sperm can get together. To date, there is no good evidence that fertility treatments pose any long-term harm to the mother. The baby may experience an increased risk of preterm birth[17] or congenital heart defects.* Both of these conditions can usually be treated successfully. We are not endorsing having fertility treatments or not. It is a personal choice. We do, however, feel it is a good idea to get an evaluation.

Importance of a Fertility Evaluation

In the United States, the protocol for couples over 35 who fail to conceive after six months of unprotected sex is to have a fertility evaluation. Some insurance plans will pay for this.** This may be a bit confusing, or lead couples to believe that you are actually supposed to be pregnant after six months of trying, when in reality, as stated above, roughly 40 percent will not be pregnant at this point.

We strongly recommend going for this exam sooner rather than later. It can be reassuring to get a clean bill of reproductive health. If, in fact, something is amiss, it is better to learn about it early on. This will give you the most time to decide how you want to proceed. Although many women start with their gynecologist, consider a reproductive endocrinologist. They receive advanced training in the nuances of the complicated hormonal

---

* Congenital birth defects were low overall, occurring among 1.2 percent of births that had involved in-vitro fertilization (IVF)/intracytoplasmic sperm injection (ICSI) and 0.5 percent of births that had not. Giorgione, V., et al., "Congenital Heart Defects in IVF/ICSI Pregnancy: Systematic Review and Meta-Analysis." *Ultrasound in Obstetrics & Gynecology* 51, no. 1 (January 2018): 33–42.

**RESOLVE, the National Infertility Organization, provides resources on insurance benefits for infertility on its website: www.resolve.org/family-building-options/insurance_coverage/state-coverage.html.

cascades that control fertility. A good fertility clinic will have flexible hours, knowledgeable staff, and offer an array of services and supports. They will not recommend an intervention until a full evaluation has been completed. They also typically have a finance person who will explain the potential costs.

Some couples resist going for a fertility evaluation because they think it is an admission of failure or mistakenly believe that this will commit them to fertility treatments. Neither is the case. It is more like a preventive health exam, ensuring everything is OK and potentially saving time and heartache if something is wrong. At the initial fertility workup, the doctor will evaluate your and your partner's sexual health, general health, and family history of infertility as well as order blood work (to test hormones) and a semen analysis.

Some couples resist going for a fertility evaluation because they think it is an admission of failure or mistakenly believe that this will commit them to fertility treatments. Neither is the case.

Male Fertility

One common misconception is that a man's fertility stays high throughout his lifetime. Although men have the ability to produce sperm throughout their life, the quality and quantity of that sperm nosedives with age.[18] This decline may start as early as age 22. One meta-review (a large study that analyzes lots of research) explored the total effect of aging on male reproductive health and found that as men age, they experience a decrease in hormone levels, which affects everything from sperm production, quantity, and quality to sexual drive.[19] Although the greatest impact is seen over age 40, decline is continuous throughout a lifetime. Most men are still fertile after age 40, but it may take longer to achieve a pregnancy. Among couples that experience infertility, about 40 percent can be traced to a male factor.[20] We have found that male infertility is an even more taboo subject than female infertility.

Your husband may be disappointed to hear that diet affects sperm quality and count. It has long been understood that zinc and folate supplements can improve sperm count.[21] Recent research shows that an overall healthy diet can improve sperm count, concentration, and motility. This study, conducted in the Netherlands, focused on men who were slightly older (an average age of 36) and defined "healthy" diet as low fat with a focus on vegetables, fruit, fish, chicken, low saturated fat, and whole grains.[22] So throw some salmon on the grill and slip him a multi-vitamin.

A reproductive endocrinologist typically does the man's initial evaluation. Often this is done at a fertility center by the same provider treating his wife (or partner). Typically, they do a semen analysis. To put it bluntly, the man masturbates into a large cup, then gives it to a lab attendant. The lab looks for the number of sperm and how quickly they swim. Some providers will also order a post-coital test. As the name implies, you have sex, then go to the doctor. Your doctor will tell you how many hours post-coital you should arrive. In this painless test, they then take a sample from the woman's cervix to see how the sperm are doing. Hours after sex, some sperm still have yet to pass through the doorway of the cervix into the uterus. Those still outside the uterus should still be alive and swimming like mad. If not, the problem may be the sperm or the vaginal environment.

In the next four chapters, you will hear stories from women with different fertility challenges. You will see their unique responses to their situations and the varied paths they take. Again, we emphasize that there is no correct way of approaching fertility. We do hope you will glean some common themes and coping techniques from these stories. Particularly, pay attention to how the couples use flexibility and humor during their journey. We offer more advice on navigating your course, because as you will read in these narratives, it is often not linear. These women also found connecting with others and mindfulness to be important coping techniques.

We cannot overemphasize how important and normal it is to take your own path armed with accurate information. We hope that the following narratives inspire you and the coping techniques empower you.

6 Staying Pregnant

You already learned this in a biology class at some point, but let us quickly remind you how a baby is formed. Two half cells (egg and sperm) unite to form one whole cell. That's followed by multiple cell divisions that lead to the trillions of cells compiled in a very perfect way that forms an entire person. That means every cell division presents an opportunity for something to go wrong. When you think about it that way, it is amazing that it ever works correctly. So for many women, getting pregnant feels like the finish line, and that positive pregnancy test forms a straight line to a healthy baby. For other women, the elation of pregnancy is followed by loss, and this tends to cast a shadow of anxiety over future pregnancies.

As Emma described in Chapter 1, her first pregnancy ended in a kind of a miscarriage called a "missed abortion" in which the fetus dies but the mother does not experience any bleeding or other signs that something has gone wrong.

Emma's Story

I felt devastated and determined to start again. In addition to starting acupuncture treatments, I treated my sorrow with brooding, self-pity, and over-analyzing the available information. My job involved researching the medical literature related to reproductive health, and every day I slipped from whatever I was supposed to be researching to identifying the causes of miscarriage or determining the optimal timing for conception after a miscarriage. I started to realize how little is known about this and how unpredictable things are at the individual level.

A few months later, I had a weird incident. My period was a few days late, and I took a pregnancy test. The positive line showed up very faintly. I can't remember all the details, because it was such an emotional and stressful time. The short version is that I was put on progesterone to try to help sustain the pregnancy. The drug made me really drowsy. Meanwhile, my pregnancy hormone levels were tested every few days and didn't rise enough. When I started bleeding after a week or two, we knew the pregnancy was over.

I felt very defeated and worried that I would never be able to conceive. Meanwhile, I was suddenly surrounded by pregnancies. One day I went to a work meeting and was forced to chat with a hugely pregnant woman. I tried to talk about some non-pregnancy-related topic, but she kept bringing the conversation around to her imminent joy. Another day I went to a hot yoga class and—guess what?—the instructor was pregnant and wove her reflections on pregnancy into ninety minutes of sweaty asanas. I couldn't help thinking how ironic it was that I avoided hot yoga when I was pregnant because I thought it could harm the fetus.

PREGTIQUETTE

Your Pregnant Friend or Colleague Complains Non-Stop About Her Pregnancy

When you are trying to conceive, it's very hard to hear other people complain about their pregnancies. Yes, there are often good reasons when people complain, and we aren't suggesting you should be uncompassionate. Still, when you are trying to conceive and would give anything to feel morning sickness, it may feel difficult to be supportive.

Here's our advice on handling others' complaints.

A WORK SCENARIO

Response Option 1: For a colleague, it may be best to redirect and avoid. For example, if you are at a meeting, redirect to the purpose of the meeting. "I'm sorry you're having a hard time. Let's get started talking about this project." If she stops by your office, then you could say: "I'm sorry, I've heard pregnancy can be rough. I do need to focus on this report right now." This is easier since talking about personal things at work is inappropriate in general (although everyone does it.) You also have no obligation to provide your colleagues with day-to-day emotional support. Chances are, other women at work who have been through pregnancy will be more than happy to discuss the trials of pregnancy and childbirth.

A FRIEND SCENARIO

For a friend who wants to share, this scenario is a bit trickier. By definition, love and support in a good friendship is unconditional and enduring. Step back and ask yourself,

In response to my despair, my acupuncturist loaned me a book on the Chinese medicine perspective on nutrition. I had been mostly vegetarian since I was about 18 years old, eating fish occasionally. It was one of my core values, and I'd never been tempted to eat meat. In fact, I even had judgmental thoughts about non-vegetarians. But according to Chinese medicine, eating meat would help correct my kidney yang deficiency. So, I are there times you complained about things she would be overjoyed to have: a husband, a house, a cool job? Was she supportive? This doesn't mean you don't get to set some boundaries. If she is dominating every conversation with her pregnancy talk or never asks about your life, then you may want to say something. This is not only for your benefit, but also for hers. Venting about a problem can be therapeutic. However, obsessing on it tends to make it worse.

Response Option 1: "I'm really sorry this pregnancy is so rough for you. I'm wondering if it might be better for you to focus on some other things right now. It seems that this is all you talk about. I'm concerned it's making you feel worse. Maybe we should talk about other things?"

Response Option 2: "I have to be honest, and please understand I'm only saying this because I care so deeply about you and our friendship. It's really hard for me to hear non-stop about how bad your pregnancy is. I understand you are having a rough time, and I want to support you, but I would also love to be pregnant. Can we spend some time talking about other things? Of course, I'm here when you need to vent about the pregnancy, as well."

started eating meat. If my acupuncturist had told me that killing the cow myself would increase my fertility, I might have become a butcher's apprentice.

During this time, I also saw an obstetrician who ran a few tests and found everything to be normal. She told me my case was not worth an intensive medical work-up, and that women aren't considered high-risk until after four or five miscarriages.

She was pleasant and hopeful, but I couldn't help wondering if there really was nothing wrong or if she didn't have a test to determine what was wrong.

Then we got a puppy, and I poured all my maternal energy into caring for him. I walked him twice a day, biked home at lunchtime to let him out of his crate, and awoke to let him outside in the middle of the night. I think that the puppy cured my fertility problem, although I feel silly writing that, because a few months later, I got pregnant again. When I told my husband, his response was something like, "Don't get your hopes up." I didn't.

The first trimester was filled with ominous bleeding episodes. I rented a fetal heart monitor and checked the baby's heartbeat obsessively. After months of fretting, I had a healthy baby girl, who is now one of the brightest people I know. Fourteen months after my daughter was born, I had one menstrual cycle, barely had any sex during the following month, and unintentionally got pregnant. My pregnancy was a breeze, and I had my second daughter at 37. She was a healthy and delightfully content baby. I felt then, and still feel, like I have an embarrassment of riches.

Hopeful Eggspectations

The title of this book echoes a common fear for women who are trying to conceive later in life—that many of their eggs are no longer viable. Miscarriages are common; probably half of all conceptions end in miscarriage, but since most have not been recognized yet as pregnancies they don't get reported. Among pregnancies that have been identified, the miscarriage rate is about 15 percent.[23]

After a miscarriage, women's main fear is that they will never be able to have a healthy baby, but there isn't research to support this fear. Although miscarriage can be physically and emotionally taxing—and a new pregnancy does not replace the fetus that was lost—statistically, only 1–5 percent of women experience two, three, or more miscarriages (which is termed recurrent miscarriage).

As the obstetrician told Emma, even among women who experience recurrent miscarriage, the outlook is considered quite optimistic. For example, one study followed a group of women who had recurrent miscarriages and found that 74 percent of them got pregnant the next time around and had healthy babies.[24] Of the eleven women that had a miscarriage or nonviable pregnancy during the study, six of these had healthy pregnancies after the study ended.

Another concern women face is how long to wait after a miscarriage. On the one hand, it seems wise to let the body heal. On the other hand, waiting can be agony, especially in the context of the idea that fertility declines over time. One study from the Netherlands included women with two or more unexplained miscarriages and found that these women got pregnant about as quickly as other women—56 percent were pregnant by six months, 74 percent after a year, and 86 percent after two years. Although this does not prove that waiting six months to conceive has a benefit, it suggests that most women do not wait, and usually their pregnancies are fine. One exception may be women whose miscarriage requires a dilation and curettage (commonly called D&C) or who have had a therapeutic abortion.[25]

After a miscarriage, women's main fear is that they will never be able to have a healthy baby, but there isn't research to support this fear.

7 Crossing the Red Line

Assisted reproductive technology (ART) is an umbrella term that includes everything from fairly simple interventions, like taking a medication to boost ovulation, to more complex processes, such as hiring a surrogate. Some people begin their fertility journey with fixed views about ART. For example, we have already met Charlotte who said she never seriously considered using any of it. Later, you will meet other women who felt that they would take any medical help that was available. Many of us start out somewhere in between, partly because we do not even understand what all the choices are. The field of ART is a forest of acronyms (TTC, IUI, IVF, FSH, etc., etc.) that could intimidate even a major science geek. We offer an abridged glossary at the end of this chapter.

Next, we meet Robin, who had a typically unpredictable story of fertility treatments. Like all of the woman we have met so far, she spent her twenties actively avoiding pregnancy, then had a change of heart in her thirties, which she described as a "slow process" of moving from ambivalence to certainty. As with Charlotte and Sharon, her partner also moved gradually from reluctance to enthusiasm. After marriage and stopping the birth control pill, Robin said she did not worry about her own fertility. Her primary care doctor ran some routine tests and said everything was fine. However, as months and then years passed without a positive pregnancy test, she experienced more stress.

Robin's Story

The months took on three distinct segments: the lead-up, ovulation, and waiting. The arrival of my period at the end of each cycle began to bring on a profound sense of disappointment, and the thought of waiting another twenty-eight days for our next shot at a positive pregnancy test often seemed unbearable. Mostly, though, I was convinced that we just hadn't aligned things well enough, and as soon as we got that timing right, I'd be waddling around and avoiding soft cheeses.

> The arrival of my period at the end of each cycle began to bring on a profound sense of disappointment, and the thought of waiting another twenty-eight days for our next shot at a positive pregnancy test often seemed unbearable.

More than three years after going off birth control but still not pregnant, my husband and I finally visited a fertility endocrinologist. I was about to turn 39 years old, still just over a year from the dreaded 40 milestone, the age at which I had decided I should "start to worry" if not already pregnant.

After we waited another six months, the endocrinologist informed us that we had plenty to worry about. While tests indicated that my ovarian reserves were within normal range, this came with a big caveat: "for my age." The news on my husband's side was even more grim: tests revealed problems in sperm count, mobility, and morphology. The endocrinologist recommended follow-up testing and a visit to the urologist for Matt, but told us that our only real option was going to be IVF. The news was shocking and devastating.

The diagnosis revealed our very different ways of processing bad news. Not satisfied with only the doctor's pamphlets on male infertility, which warned against the hazards of hot tubs, alcohol, underwear, and stress, I googled incessantly and became obsessed with the possibility that Matt's cell phone signal was killing his sperm, among other things. I immediately re-placed all of my husband's briefs with loose boxers, spent $200 on supplements, and instructed him to stop taking baths and drinking beer. I explored acupuncturists specializing in fertility who recommended cutting all dairy and wheat from his diet.

Needless to say, some of these changes were easier to implement than others. While new underwear and a serious vitamin regimen were relatively easy to accept, a bath and a beer (or three) were Matt's after-work relaxation routine. Giving these up also meant adding significant stress, which the sperm optimization guidance warned against. In the end, he replaced baths with showers, limited drinking, and started making more health-conscious food choices. I tried (but often failed) to withhold judgment and eventually accepted that the stress of adopting a gluten-free diet would most likely cancel out any benefit.

The news of our infertility also revealed the ways in which we had unconsciously put into place all the pieces to start a family. We did grown-up things like contribute monthly to retirement and savings accounts in hopes of someday purchasing a home in the insane New York housing market. I had worked for the same nonprofit for over eight years, moving from an entry-level position into a senior management role. My job could be extremely stressful and demand long hours, but I believed in the cause, and I'd built up a generous bank of sick and vacation time and some flexibility to work from home. We adopted a dog and became doting dog parents, then bought a car so we could travel with the dog. We opted for quiet evenings at home and were usually in bed before midnight.

The realization that children might not be part of our future cast doubt over these choices. Maybe we should use our nest egg to travel the world or start a goat farm. Maybe it was time for Matt to become a full-time artist, or for me to start a bakery.

Over the next year, our treatment plan evolved. The doctor originally wanted to begin IVF immediately, but after slightly more promising follow-up testing, she was open to trying up to three rounds of the less intensive and less expensive IUI. Although we had not yet done extensive research or soul-searching, I saw IVF as a sort of red line over which I would not cross. We were lucky to have insurance that would cover diagnosis and treatment, including IUI, but not IVF. Although medications could be covered, costs for the procedure itself would run us nearly $15,000 per cycle, with no guarantee of success. In contrast, adoption seemed like a process guaranteed to end with a child, although the timeline and challenges along the way were completely unpredictable. I found the financial calculation was an impossible one to make. How do you put a monetary value on a baby? I attempted to reconcile this dilemma by signing up with a fertility registry to participate in experimental treatments and also a listserv for those considering adoption. Hopefully we would not have to make that decision, but I wanted to be prepared.

The IUI protocol involved nightly injections in the stomach ("trigger shots"). I was amused by the irony that I needed to buy "old lady glasses" from the drug store to ensure I dispensed the prescribed dose of medication. As a prerequisite to IUI, I also underwent a hysterosalpingogram to rule out blocked fallopian tubes. I was informed that this could additionally boost fertility by "clearing the cobwebs" out of my fallopian tubes, another allusion to my stubbornly advancing age. Our lives became flooded with numbers and probabilities—sperm concentrations and motility percentages, number and diameter of follicles, cc's of medication at hundreds of dollars a dose. I started three to four days per week with a transvaginal ultrasound and blood draw, in addition to regular acupuncture to maximize our chances. Although intense, the close monitoring was also reassuring; we wouldn't be missing my fertile window anymore.

PREGTIQUETTE

When You Need to Cancel Plans
for Timed Sex or Fertility Treatments

Most of us are not going to say, "I can't make it to book club tonight because I think I'm ovulating and so I need to seduce Tom." If that feels like oversharing to you, a simple text or call will do. "Sorry ladies, feeling under the weather, please enjoy without me." Do not feel guilty about this. People cancel plans for all sorts of reasons. Once you have a child, you will be forced to miss all sorts of social events.

Fertility treatments or surgeries are another matter, as you may need to miss work or possibly even an important family or social event. Navigating this can be tricky. It's important to consider that once you are forthcoming about why you are cancelling, there may be pressure to follow up with the results. This is entirely dependent on who you are actually sharing the information with. Sharon needed a week off of work for an exploratory laparoscopy to rule out endometriosis. Although not an emergency, it was last minute, because they would not have done it if she had gotten pregnant that month. She was very close to her boss at the time, who knew about her fertility struggle and was very supportive and also very non-intrusive, so she felt comfortable being honest about it. Not all workplaces are like this. You certainly don't want to jeopardize your employment, so you may need to simply take a sick day if you feel it is inappropriate to share. Another option is to say, "I'm having a small surgery, nothing to worry about, but I will need a few days off." If any supervisors or co-workers ask you about it, you can simply say, "I appreciate your concern, but it's personal in nature, and I appreciate you respecting my privacy."

Matt learned how to administer the nightly shots and duti-fully produced sperm samples twice per month in a room with an oversized couch and magazines that he described as "sur-prisingly hardcore." Despite some relatively promising sperm counts and my body's decent response to ovulation induction, all three IUI's failed.

I had already realized that I was not ready to give up on having a baby, and Matt wisely recognized that if we did not give IVF a try, I'd always regret it. In the end, we decided that home ownership could wait. We spent much of the savings we were extremely fortunate to have put away and got some addi-tional help from my parents. Meanwhile, fertility surrounded us. At work, I nearly had to leave a meeting when a coworker announced her pregnancy. Another revealed that she, at four years my junior, was about to welcome her first grandchild. Facebook became a minefield of birth announcements, sono-gram pictures, and other reminders that the rest of the world was busy making babies. Holidays were particularly difficult. Matt's sister became pregnant with her fourth and then fifth child. We spent each Thanksgiving with them, watching her family grow as we impatiently waited for ours to begin.

Other social interactions, however, were a huge source of support. It was cathartic to joke with other childless friends about our dusty old wombs. I was surprised to learn I had sev-eral friends—some with children and some without—who had struggled with infertility. It was especially helpful to bond with others who spoke the language of ART. It was those friends who really understood what it's like to undergo transvaginal ultra-sounds several times a week, or to know the disappointment of a retrieval that yields only three eggs when the ultrasound showed eight.

We converted our first round of IVF to IUI after my body failed to respond as expected to the prescribed cocktail of Ganirelix, Menopur, and Gonal-F, but my reaction was one of relief rather than disappointment. I had heard about other women yielding fifteen to twenty eggs at retrieval. My five seemed pathetic, and I was sure I could do better. After a modestly stronger response on a modified regimen, we proceeded with retrieval and in-tra-cytoplasmic sperm injection (ICSI) and transferred three of four embryos that survived to day three, but our first full IVF cycle was unsuccessful.

After that, Thanksgiving, Christmas, and work deadlines meant a three-month break from treatment, but not from the monthly cycle of hopefulness followed by disappointment.

In addition to bonding with those friends who had received fertility treatments, another helpful strategy I discovered was making other plans. Between the frequency of medical appointments, nightly injections, and emotional space that treatment demands, baby-making can be all-consuming. When I could manage it, involving my mind with other activities was extremely helpful, especially during the holding pattern between active treatment and the pregnancy test. Just before we were to undergo our second and final round of IVF, we received an invitation to a friend's fortieth birthday party in England. At first I dismissed the invitation as impossible, but then realized that it might be helpful to have something to look forward to. If we got lucky, I would be traveling at a good time—the beginning of my second trimester. If we didn't, I would have travel-planning to occupy my brain.

Between the frequency of medical appointments, nightly injections, and emotional space that treatment demands, baby-making can be all-consuming.

By the time we started our final round of IVF, I was beginning to settle into numb resignation. The day before I was scheduled for a blood test to determine whether our last round of IVF was successful, I did an at-home test to prepare myself. Results were negative. I was disappointed but resolute in finally terminating treatment and moving forward with adoption. That night, behind on a deadline that had taken me off guard, I worked until 4 a.m. and came very close to skipping my appointment, but I managed to drag myself in.

When the nurse called that afternoon and said she had good news, I was sure there had been a mistake. Over the following week, I used up the rest of my at-home tests just so I could see that positive result again and again. Old worries gave way to a host of new anxieties, but we made it. We welcomed our impossible little girl to the world in mid-November, sandwiched perfectly between my husband's and my forty-first birthdays. Now I cry all the time for different reasons as I realize again and again that she is real.

Our Reflection on Robin's Story

Although one of this book's messages is that every fertility journey is unique, this story may be close to average in many ways. Robin and her husband entered with humble expectations, giving things time to work out on their own, then eventually realizing that interventions were needed. They took a stepwise approach. First, adjusting diet and lifestyle, then adding acupuncture, finally turning to Western medicine.

Couples, regardless of what approach they take, often perceive the journey as a rabbit hole. They start off with the intention of "just" changing diet, or trying acupuncture, or starting Clomid and then, before they know it, they've embraced a dozen more interventions and racked up the credit card. All of the options can be confusing. We offer advice on navigating the journey in the next chapter.

For great books on Eastern medical approaches to fertility, see the recommended resources section. Below, we clarify some of the Western medical approaches. Please note, we are not reproductive endocrinologists, obstetricians, or midwives. In other words, we simply collected the information and are presenting it, but are not formally educated in it or licensed to practice it.

Having said that, you can rely on the information below to get a good general education, even though we feel it's best to seek expert opinion for information pertaining to your specific situation. We encourage you to see a licensed health professional who specializes in fertility.

Common Fertility-Related Terms

Assisted Reproductive Technology (ART). Also called fertility treatments.

Anti-Müllerian Hormone (AMH). A hormone tested by a blood test which checks ovarian reserve, aka egg supply.

Fertility Awareness Method (FAM). A systematic approach to monitoring your menstrual cycle. It involves taking a daily basal (first thing in the morning) temperature orally and monitoring cervical mucus and cervical position. It can be used to improve chances of conception or as birth control and is quite different from the rhythm method. See recommended resources section for further information.

Follicle-Stimulating Hormone (FSH). A hormone released by the pituitary gland that stimulates the growth of the follicle, which surrounds the egg. It can also be given as an injectable medication in IVF cycles.

Hysterosalpingogram (HSG). An X-ray in which dye is injected into the uterus. It helps to determine if there are any obstructions in the uterus or fallopian tubes that may be preventing conception. Some people think it may help with fertility by "cleaning out the cobwebs."

Ovarian reserve. An estimation of female fertility based on egg number and quality.

Semen analysis. Like the name implies, checks a sample of ejaculate for sperm presence, quality, and quantity.

Thyroid tests. The thyroid is the boss of the hormone system, and therefore important for fertility. Common blood tests measure Thyroid-Stimulating Hormone (TSH), Thyroxine (T4), and thyroid antibodies.

Intrauterine insemination (IUI). A procedure in which sperm are injected into the uterus directly.

Trigger shot. An injection of human chorionic gonadotropin (HCG) given to help ovulation.

Transvaginal ultrasound. This is an ultrasound that is done by inserting a wand into the vagina. It allows the fetus to be seen at an earlier phase of development, compared to the ultrasound wand that's placed on a woman's stomach later in pregnancy.

In vitro fertilization (IVF). A process in which multiple eggs are stimulated to mature and then retrieved from the woman and mixed with sperm in a laboratory dish. (Anything that happens in a laboratory is called "in vitro.") The sperm fertilize the eggs in the same way they would if inside the woman's body. They are then placed back into the woman's uterus. The egg-sperm combos at this stage of development are considered embryos. The transfer back into the womb occurs about three to five days after the retrieval. At this point, the embryos have expanded into a multi-cell form.

Intracytoplasmic sperm injection (ICSI). An augmentation to IVF in which the sperm are injected directly into the eggs. It is used primarily if there is a problem with the sperm.

Fertility Treatments and Conception Rates

Success rates for fertility treatments vary based on intervention, couple's age, and, notably, the way the clinic chooses to report them. One important question to ask is about the live birth rate. This is different (and often lower) than the conception rate. However, an important caveat to consider is that some fertility centers may have a lower live birth rate because they are willing to work with more challenging cases. This does not mean that the care is subpar. In fact, it could be very high quality. Ultimately, it is best to have open and honest discussions with your care providers about their experience and approach. You need to be comfortable and have faith in the people from whom you are receiving treatment.

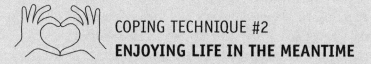

COPING TECHNIQUE #2
ENJOYING LIFE IN THE MEANTIME

Robin planned a trip to England to distract herself from worrying about her last round of IVF. At times, this advice to do something to get your mind off conception irks women trying to conceive. We get it. We've been in that place where the only thing enjoyable would be cuddling a new baby. Also, it is important to feel your feelings and process them, not just distract yourself from them. However, when circumstances require waiting, you can make yourself even more miserable by ruminating on barriers and delays. Constant brooding can harm your relationships and cause even more suffering. It can also isolate you from others, and having fulfilling relationships is necessary for happiness.

Using mindfulness (explained in Chapter 9), observe what feels good to you. This does not need to be a trip to another continent. It may be as simple as listening to your favorite music, reading, sitting outside, sipping tea, or going dancing. The list of what could work for you is endless. Try to incorporate as much of that into your life as possible. Don't feel guilty if it means giving up obligations. Remember, once you have the baby, you will be giving up lots of social, family, and work engagements. Taking care of yourself now as you would during your pregnancy or once you have a baby is completely legitimate.

Both Emma and Sharon used distraction to cope with setbacks while trying to conceive. As we described in Chapter 1, writing this book and the accompanying blog was one of Sharon's primary coping strategies. It gave her a sense of meaning and purpose, through helping others by sharing her experience. As Emma described in Chapter 6, her puppy served as an adorable distraction from her fear of miscarrying again. After she got pregnant, the woman who gave her the puppy explained that she had had five miscarriages before conceiving her daughter. She knew what the experience was like and that the puppy would be good medicine.

One thing we love about Robin's story is that she recognized the importance of self-care, including identifying her own coping techniques. She sought emotional support from those who had been in a similar situation. She also talked about making other plans.

8   **Just Keep Swimming**

T his is a story about strong barriers to motherhood—and an even stronger determination to overcome them. Few couples will endure the particular challenges that Ashley and Michael did. It is a bit frightening, really. However, we decided to include it for a few reasons. First, some of you may have similar journeys, with plenty of setbacks and frustrations. Second, we wanted to share a story from someone who was willing to try lots of different approaches. Third, we found their insights and their approach to these challenges to be inspiring and thought-provoking.

Ashley's Story

My husband and I started trying for a baby when I was 32, when most of our friends did not have children yet. We tried for six months, and when nothing happened, we got tested. After working through various tests and fertility challenges with my husband, I was eventually diagnosed with stage 4 endometriosis that compromised my uterus and fallopian tubes. A few years later, after countless and various treatments, we would joke, in a way that would be OK only if we were talking to each other, by saying things like, "Well, we're both defective. At least no more condoms, birth control pills, or fear of unplanned pregnancies for us."

This was our attempt at coping with our infertility struggles through humor, and perhaps even finding a bright side. It was frustrating, and at the same time, part of me just felt guilty for feeling sorry for myself, for us. I remember going to the gym one day and seeing someone in a wheelchair, someone who was my age and paralyzed, and thinking, "I can't believe I was just crying in the bathroom because I had a negative pregnancy test." Endometriosis is not life-threatening, and we had the marriage, the motivation, and the finances to figure out how to overcome infertility. We were lucky in so many ways; having babies easily just was not one of them.

People who knew what we were going through would remark, "That is really hard on a marriage. People get divorced over this. Are you OK?" We were pretty united all the time, but we had different approaches to the planning. I wanted to plan several steps ahead. I always wanted to find answers to the "what if's" and "what now's" before we needed them. My justification was that we would be able to hit the ground running, recover quickly from bad news, deal with it, and move on to the end goal—a child. Like Dorey in the movie Finding Nemo, my approach was to just keep swimming. My husband, Michael, would stop us from playing the "what if" game. His reasoning was that we would end up having a painful discussion or even an argument about something that would never happen. Thinking back, I think he had the right approach. I can imagine that if a couple wasn't really functioning as a team before trying to conceive, they could end up arguing all the time about a lot of hypothetical scenarios.

We received a lot of advice about managing our stress, but I could never figure out the whole de-stressing thing. People would say, "Oh, stress is the biggest obstacle to conceiving." My visceral reaction to these naïve advice-givers was, "OK, then. Why don't you explain to me how to avoid stress when you are giving yourself multiple daily injections, running to the doctor to be internally probed on a weekly basis, all while hopped up on hormones and trying to maintain some semblance of sanity in spite of such hormones?" I tried acupuncture, because I thought it would help, but I found it painful. Yoga was the opposite of stress-relieving, for me, because it gave me plenty of time to re-flect on all the things that were going wrong.

The only thing that helped me de-stress was to focus on other things. We would think of things that would be more difficult to do if we had an infant, and then we would do them. We picked travel as our consolation prize to ourselves. We spent one New Year's Eve in New Orleans and one in Paris, and also took a long and fabulous trip to New Zealand—all of which (we told ourselves) would have been difficult or impossible with children.

I was lucky to become pregnant when I was 35 through IVF, but at the end of my first trimester, my obstetrician diagnosed me with placenta previa, in which the placenta grows too close to the cervix, creating increased risk for dangerous bleeding). She said that 85–90 percent of cases would resolve before it was time to deliver. It never resolved and eventually she put me on what we called "house arrest." I was confined to resting on a mattress as much as possible (sitting or lying down), due to the risk that I could start bleeding heavily at any time, and if I was home I could easily call 911. Despite this, I felt happy and well and was able to work full-time from home. Of course, I had some minor discomfort. I noticed that my pants had sud-denly become really tight, and I had heartburn and a few bad headaches, which at the time I considered to be normal third trimester symptoms.

A few weeks before my due date, my mother's friend sur-prised me by inviting friends to my house for a baby shower. I felt fine and even elated at the shower, but I didn't have much of an appetite, and later that night I felt exhausted and had a headache and swollen ankles. I thought it was because of the excitement and possibly not drinking enough water. I also had a weird pain in my shoulder blades. That night I couldn't sleep, so I moved from bed to the mattress in my living room, where I would sit and telecommute during the day. The next thing that I remember was nurses and doctors trying to talk to me in the hospital, asking when I last felt movement from the baby—and saying that they could not find a heartbeat.

AVA ARRIVES

I don't remember much about the day Ava was born—32 weeks into my pregnancy. As Michael recounts the story, he came to the living room and found me sleeping on my stomach and tried to wake me up. Then I had a seizure. He called 911 and an ambulance rushed me to the hospital. At some point, they found Ava's heartbeat, and they were able to bring my high blood pressure (which had caused the seizure) down, but my liver and kidneys started to fail. At that point, they had to take me for an emergency C-section.

When I woke up the next day, Michael told me that she had arrived, that she was beautiful and doing well. He took me to the NICU so I could see her. Of course, I didn't recognize her. There was no immediate mother-child bond that is lovingly described in all the parent-prep books. But as I held her for the first, second, and third times, she was mine and I hers. She did not arrive the way we planned, but just in the way she was meant to arrive.

I was in the hospital for a week while they tried to control the after-effects of eclampsia (high blood pressure) and placenta accreta, a complication in which the placenta grows too deeply into the uterine wall. (The fluid retention that made my pants feel tight and the headache had been warning signs of pre-eclampsia.) Plus, I had dislocated my shoulder during the seizure. Ava was in the NICU for twenty-eight days, but was healthy despite being born prematurely at three pounds, six ounces.

A SIBLING FOR AVA

I always knew that I wanted a second child, largely because I really value my relationships with my siblings. I was lucky, because the emergency room doctor who saw me was a nationally renowned expert on high-risk pregnancy. She said there was no reason that I couldn't be pregnant again, although she recommended that I take a year to recover. The complications that I experienced with the first pregnancy would not necessarily occur in a second pregnancy.

It took me a while to convince Michael that I should ever be pregnant again. He felt very traumatized by the birth experience, because at one point the doctors told him that I might not survive. Plus, he's an only child and pointed out that lots of people do not have great relationships with their siblings. So the two of us met with my obstetrician, and Michael grilled her with questions before agreeing to try again.

The summer after Ava turned one, we agreed to try a few more rounds of IVF. There's a huge difference in fertility treatments when you don't have any kids versus when you already have one. I cannot say it is easier or harder, just different. When the treatments did not lead to conception, I grieved for us and also for Ava not having a sibling to grow up with.

TRYING SURROGACY AND ADOPTION

Both my amazing sisters offered to serve as gestational carriers (surrogates). We chose my youngest sister, who was unmarried, lived nearby, and had no children. Through the evaluation process, she found out that she had endometriosis, too, and had surgery to correct it. I think she had two or three rounds of IVF—I can't remember exactly—but the last time we had decided in advance that it would be the last time. She got pregnant, but miscarried at nine or ten weeks.

It was a lot harder going through the process with my sister, because you're not just managing your own emotions. I always felt like I had to be in the supportive big sister role. It was very hard. She was all hopped up on the hormones. I felt like I couldn't be upset, that I had to comfort her first. It led to a host of different challenges that I hadn't thought about.

[After that, Ashley and Michael decided to try to adopt a baby within the United States, but not in their home state, where birth mothers have thirty days to change their minds about adoption. After extensive research, they chose a law firm, rather than an adoption agency. They were asked to create a brochure to market themselves to potential birth mothers, which their law firm also posted on an independent website. The law firm sent monthly status updates and suggested that the process would take about a year. They said that typically birth mothers are matched with adoptive parents during the third trimester, making it less likely that the birth mother will change her mind. They said that there was a 5 percent chance of an emergency match, meaning that after a baby was born, sometimes the parents who had been selected to adopt don't follow through. They waited for months and then...]

On Easter Sunday, when Ava was five years old, I got an unexpected call from a counselor that worked for a website where we had posted our adoptive parent information. She told me that a little girl had been born that morning on the other side of the state where we lived. The family that she had selected months ago backed out via a text message while she was in labor. Needless to say, she was upset, panicked, and scared. Michael and I hesitated for about ten minutes. We were shocked and excited, but were petrified of the thirty-day waiting period in our state. In our state, for thirty days after the baby is released to the adoptive parents, either birth parent may change their mind—for any reason.

After we spoke to her via phone, the birth mother asked to meet with us in person, and we drove to meet her in the hospital the next day. We were incredibly nervous, still in shock, and wondering how to handle the first meeting with the birth mother and the little baby who might become our daughter. As we exited the hospital elevator and walked down the hall to her room,

Michael whispered to me, "Your fly is down." It wasn't. We both laughed, and the stress was deflated for just a few seconds.

We met the birth mother, her current boyfriend (not the birth father), and the baby we would name Emily. I had always envisioned that if we found ourselves in this situation someone would be with us to make introductions and explain boundaries. It was clear that the birth mother had agonized over her decision to place her daughter with adoptive parents. She had two young daughters from a prior marriage (and different birth father) and absolutely could not financially take on another child. She is an amazing person and I am, and will always be, amazed at her bravery and selflessness at reaching this decision.

We met Emily, held her, fed her, and changed her diapers. We spent all day getting to know the birth mother, and actually negotiated with the hospital for another day of hospitalization before discharge. She wanted one more day to get to know us, and we fully supported that decision.

Because of our state's laws, the birth mother had to walk out of the hospital with the baby, rather than releasing her to us in the hospital room. So the birth mother, our attorney, and Michael and I walked out of the hospital together, the birth mother holding Emily. Then she handed Emily over to us in the parking lot. We were all crying and hugging, unsure of what to say and how to say goodbye. We had always pictured a celebratory mood when we picked up our adoptive daughter—beaming smiles and happy tears. But this was not that—we cried for the birth mother's loss and pain. We drove out of the hospital parking lot with Emily in the back seat, wiping our tears, in shock and awe of the birth mother and her kindness and love for Emily.

We took Emily home, and I lost fifteen pounds during the thirty-day waiting period. It was a stressful time, although there was never any indication that the birth mother would change her mind. We texted messages and photos about twenty to thirty times each day. After what seemed like thirty years, the *thirty days ended, but our relationship with the birth mother, thankfully, did not.*

By mutual agreement, we stay in touch with the birth mother via photos, text messages, and bi-annual visits. It makes us happy to know that Emily will be able to know that her birth mother loves her and did not abandon her. This is also tremendously important to the birth mother. She can witness for herself that Emily is healthy, outrageously happy, and surrounded by so many people that love her fiercely.

I don't know if our story is unique—it feels unique to us. At every stage of our path, the one thing that was consistent was that nothing went according to the plan. At every stage, we became really focused on what we were going to do, but bobbed, weaved, and just kept swimming when that turned out to be the wrong path. After we became a family of four, we started to exhale and began to joke about the ridiculousness of the journey. But how we love our bottom line—two beautiful kids, with such unique stories that they ask to be told over and over again.

Our Reflection on Ashley's Story

Ashley and Michael found moments of lightness even through the most trying of circumstances. They focused on joy and, more importantly, what brought them joy. They sought those experiences. As their circumstances changed, they adapted to them instead of resisting their reality. This is essential for all aspects of life. Learning to bend with your circumstances, changing your course as needed, and laughing will help you attain the life you want and live well while doing so.

Is Stress Part of the Problem?

Unless you are like Erin and have a less planned, boating-related pregnancy, the fertility journey tends to induce stress. Then women frequently worry that the stress is having a negative impact on their fertility. The scientific literature around mood and fertility is a bit confusing, especially because it focuses on people having trouble trying to conceive, not those who easily conceive. For example, we don't know the emotional states nor self-care practices of couples that easily conceive. Maybe they are stressed out too. Maybe they spend all their time on social media instead of meditating and drinking herbal tea.

Make no mistake, we are not saying "just relax and it will happen."

One question, researchers have repeatedly asked is, are there fundamental psychological differences between women who have trouble conceiving and those that don't? A meta review exploring forty years of research on the topic came back inconclusive.[26] There were just as many studies showing increased psychological symptoms in women struggling with fertility as there were studies showing the opposite. The studies also encountered the same problem of assessing women after fertility treatment was initiated, so we don't have a clear idea if they were suffering from depression or anxiety at baseline, which may have contributed to infertility, or if the infertility ultimately causes the psychological despair. However, we do know that reduced stress levels are correlational (associated with, but not necessarily causal) to improved health outcomes in many areas, from heart disease to chronic pain. For all people in all situations, reduced stress simply feels better.

Alice Domar, PhD, and colleagues demonstrated reduced stress symptoms in a large sample of women who were experiencing fertility challenges by having them participate in a structured therapy group in which they learned coping skills.[27] In another study, couples undergoing IVF who participated in a mind-body group showed improved conception rates compared to couples in a control group.[28] The sample size was small, but considering there were no harmful side effects of this intervention, the approach is promising. (Follow-up studies could examine if the skills learned in the group could also be applied to dealing with the stress of a screaming toddler.)

Make no mistake, we are not saying "just relax and it will happen." There's no actual proof of that, plus it's demeaning. It invalidates all of the emotions around struggling to conceive and also implies that the stressed-out couple is to blame.

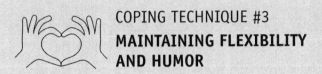

COPING TECHNIQUE #3
MAINTAINING FLEXIBILITY
AND HUMOR

You may have a basic framework for starting a family. At the very least, going off of birth control is necessary. Preparing your body for a healthy pregnancy is ideal. The rest evolves along with the journey. Some women approach conception with a relaxed attitude. They are the "throw away the condoms and drink some wine" bunch. Other women are a bit type A. They track ovulation and have perfectly timed intercourse. Which are more successful? Both! This is great news. You don't have to change who you are to conceive.

It is helpful, however, to adapt if your method is not working. If you are not conceiving or the process is becoming too stressful for you, it may be time to rethink things. This is a time to challenge your beliefs and explore options. If you are trying to do everything perfectly, maybe you need to step back and have a few months of unplanned, untimed intercourse. Conversely, as we described in Chapter 5, having a fertility evaluation can add a wealth of knowledge. If you have been relaxed about the process, but are starting to feel panicked, it may be worth scheduling an appointment at your fertility center simply to get a basic work up.

Understanding that life is dynamic rather than static can actually be reassuring. Ashley and Michael moved from IVF to surrogacy to adoption. As one road no longer seemed promising, they explored a new one. With fertility, the picture is always changing. Perhaps IVF was not an option in the past, but you can reconsider this choice if you get a new job that has health insurance benefits that will cover the cost. Perhaps your husband was resistant to getting a semen analysis, but after months of seeing you cry with every period is now willing to do it. The 5 percent chance is unlikely, but sometimes it happens. Keeping your mind and heart open to options and new information is essential to your well-being.

Laugh

Laughter is one antidote to stress. We love this saying, which has been attributed to several great comedians: "Tragedy plus time equals comedy." The women whose stories are included in this book have a lot to laugh about—in retrospect. Have fun with yourself. The situation may be serious, but you don't have to take yourself so seriously. If you became the sex Nazi demanding sex in specific positions at specific fertile peak times, learn to laugh at how obscene that really is. Anyone who has dealt with a fertility clinic knows that they are ripe with comedic relief. Sharon once received a voicemail from the clinic nurse on a Saturday morning instructing her to have sex on Sunday and Monday. She and her husband were rolling on the floor laughing. It's not a voicemail she ever expected to receive from anyone, let alone a health professional.

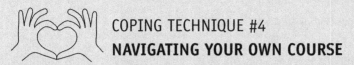

COPING TECHNIQUE #4
NAVIGATING YOUR OWN COURSE

"Though there is no replacement for developing and honing our women's wisdom—that inner guidance that helps us choose which roads to take and which ones to avoid—I've found this inner guidance works best when it's balanced with good, solid, up-to-date information."

– Dr. Christiane Northrup, *Women's Bodies, Women's Wisdom*

Ashley and Michael made many decisions about treatment options throughout their long journey. For better or worse, there are many options available to have children. Surrogacy and adoption are at the extreme end. More commonly, you will be faced with different techniques for improving fertility. Some couples have told us that they felt pressured to take a certain action quickly to maximize their chances of success. And as described previously, we can guarantee that if you tell people you are trying to conceive, they will barrage you with advice. It's key to remember that you are free to do what you want. You are also free to change your mind. For example, Robin at first saw IVF as the red line, but then she changed her mind.

Nearly every woman interviewed for this book found a behavior or regimen that she thought was one of the keys to her success. We provide our advice, too. For example, we share a list of our favorite fertility advice books in the recommended resources section. Many of them list diets and activities that are great for our general health, because it is well established that eating a lot of fresh vegetables and limiting processed food is good for you. The guide for choosing what you do is up to you. Before embracing any practice, diet, or supplement, ask yourself three key questions to figure out what is best for you:

• **How does this feel to me?**

• **Why do I think this will help?**

• **How will doing this affect my relationship? My finances?**

We explore these questions further in the rest of this chapter.

How does this feel to me? If you are sensing dread around doing something, then it is probably not a good thing. One diet from an e-book on fertility touts consuming twenty ounces of whole-fat dairy per day. Even if that worked, it would surely wreak havoc on your cholesterol and weight. Weigh the pros and cons of any plan, and only pursue it if you feel that, overall, it's worth it. For example, you may love yoga but can only fit a 6 a.m. class into your schedule. As much as you hate getting up early, it is probably worth doing if you'll feel better the rest of the day and you believe it will help your fertility. If you dread doing it, then it will only create a stress response that could hurt you more than help you.

Why do I think this will help? Does the practice fit with your core values and what are the credentials of its practitioners/proponents? Some people jump into Western medicine (i.e., Clomid, IUI, IVF) and others are much more comfortable with traditional Chinese medicine (acupuncture and herbs). Regardless, make sure it is a good fit emotionally, morally, and financially. Ask yourself, "Why am I doing this?" Just because your sister got pregnant on Clomid doesn't mean it's a good fit for you. Research the practitioners to ensure they are experienced and well trained in their discipline. This is true for the Western route as well as the Eastern; not every ob-gyn is a fertility expert, just like not everyone who dispenses herbs understands them.

How will doing this affect my relationship and finances? If you are trying to have a baby with a partner, you have to work together to find an approach that is agreeable. Regular, honest communication is essential. Perhaps your husband is supportive of you going to yoga glass, but is worried about the cost. In this case, find a community class at a reduced rate. Sharon's husband couldn't tolerate the smell of the Chinese herbs she was prescribed to take in tea form. The compromise was to prepare them in a crockpot on their back porch. (We will never know what the neighbors thought!) Think in terms of "yes, and..." versus "no, but...." This means, look for a way to have your needs met in a fashion that doesn't tread on your partner's needs. Calmly explain why the practice is important to you and actively listen to his concerns. When you both have all of the information, you can find a solution.

It is easy to become overwhelmed by all of the fertility advice and to lose sight of which aspects are within your control. Consider keeping a spreadsheet to help you track what is working for you and what is not. "Working for you" doesn't mean getting pregnant, it means helping you feel healthy and good and proactive while trying to do so. Refer to the spreadsheet weekly to check in with yourself honestly. Here's an example:

Practice	Start Date	How well is this working?
HERBS	7/1/2017	7/15/17 *The tea tastes terrible, is expensive, and Tom complains of the smell.*
ACUPUNCTURE	7/1/2017	7/15/17 *Love it!* 8/1/17 *Still enjoy it, but it is stressful to get to appointments on time.*

In this example, things may require readjusting. For example, you could find a walk-in acupuncture clinic or one that offers Saturday hours if getting to appointments on time is too stressful. You could ask if the herbs are available in a tablet preparation if your partner can't stand the smell, or decide to stop them altogether if they cost too much. Remember, you cannot control the outcome, but you can control your choices and actions during the journey.

Next, we meet Elizabeth, who faced a completely different set of circumstances and took a radically different approach to conceiving.

9 Invitation and Surrender

E lizabeth was thoughtful about major life choices, postponing marriage and children until she felt the time was right. She met Kevin in her twenties but waited several years after he proposed to get married because she wanted to be sure they were both truly ready. Like other couples we interviewed, their desire for children changed over time, from uncertainty to a strong yearning. In Elizabeth's case, becoming an aunt was one of the main factors. So they officially started trying to conceive ten years into their relationship. Then she received shocking news and ended up making major lifestyle changes.

Elizabeth's Story

I was 35 when we actively started trying to conceive. It was partly because of my age but more because we were at that place in our lives where we felt more settled. We just sort of went by the cycle. I never got pregnant, and it was disappointing each month. At the same time, I was working two jobs that were very physically demanding. I was wired all the time, and had episodes of emotional eating when I would consume a lot of sugar, dairy products, and caffeine. I also was not grounded at all.

After more than one year of trying to conceive, I found a lump in my breast while doing a self-exam. After being told—over the phone—that I had cancer, I was devastated and felt overcome with despair. Life came to a drastic halt. I also wondered if cancer had affected my ability to conceive. The diagnosis felt like an intense wake-up call and left me yearning for a child even more.

In June, I had a lumpectomy in one breast. They recommended doing a lumpectomy in both breasts, but I wanted to have one intact breast so I could experience breastfeeding. One doctor urged me to have an oophorectomy (removal of ovaries). Again, I said no, because it would have prevented me from getting pregnant.

In October, I had radiation. In between, we saw two different fertility specialists. The first one described how I could freeze my eggs and do IVF later. It was really overwhelming to me. So, I sought somebody else, who also overwhelmed us with folders full of information about the different treatments, the costs, and the likelihood of success. I was put off by the idea of taking a lot of medications in order to carry a child. After being treated for cancer, I wanted to cleanse my body, and taking fertility meds would be counter-intuitive. Plus, I had always preferred taking a natural approach to my health care, and felt in my heart that it was how I wanted to approach this fertility journey. Cost was also an issue, especially since there was no guarantee that I would get pregnant. We decided not to use IVF, mainly because it felt right to us.

The breast cancer diagnosis was devastating, but it gave me the courage to make some positive changes in my life.

One thing we felt clear on was that I wouldn't take the breast cancer medication Tamoxifen, which causes menopausal symptoms. One of my oncologists wanted me to take it for five years, which would have meant waiting until my early forties before trying to conceive. Instead, I have regular monitoring to check for cancer.

After this, in addition to recovering from the shock of the cancer diagnosis and treatment, I felt a deep sadness that we would never conceive. However, there was a hopeful side of me that still thought anything was possible. I never lost hope completely; I had heard of so many women in their forties conceiving and giving birth to healthy children.

A good friend recommended acupuncture and Chinese herbs, so I researched acupuncturists in my area. The acupuncturist recommended starting to take my temperature every morning, and really paying attention to my cycle and when I was ovulating, which I did. My acupuncturist was really supportive because she had conceived during her late thirties.

In addition to keeping track of my cycle and getting acupuncture regularly, I tried to radically change my diet, did qigong every day, started meditating, took Chinese herbs, and massaged acupressure points related to fertility. I also enjoyed googling about fertility and the yoga poses, herbs, supplements, etc., that could support conception. I would try things if the website looked legitimate or if I'd heard about it from a friend, but still we were doing crazy things! For example, after sex, I would do a yoga pose with my legs in the air!

The only medical procedure I had was a hysterosalpingogram toward the end of the year after my cancer diagnosis. Out of all the list of different things that you could do, that seemed the easiest and the least invasive.

After a few months of these changes, my mood really improved. I think that getting the chi (energy) flowing from acupuncture and qigong really lifted my spirits. I realize now that stress and poor diet can create stagnant energy in the body, so addressing it with acupuncture, qigong, and a cleaner diet helped my body create balance and a more fertile environment. Also, in the fall of the year after my diagnosis I quit one of my jobs because it was really stressful, which helped restore my health too.

[Kevin was supportive of Elizabeth's choices but felt they couldn't continue the acupuncture indefinitely.]

I guess I sort of put it out there in the universe. That sounds kind of new age-y, but I said, "I'm surrendering. What is the plan for me?" So I left it open. I decided to give myself to the end of the year, and if I didn't conceive, I would fill my life with other things. This was my way of making peace with it by learning to accept the unknown. Practicing daily mindfulness meditation helped me to be less reactive and more at peace. I felt all kinds of emotions: anticipation, sadness, hopefulness alternating with frustration, anxiety, and, ultimately, worry that time was running out.

TALKING TO MY UNBORN CHILD'S SPIRIT

During one of the last treatments with my acupuncturist, she asked, "Have you spoken to the spirit of this baby to invite it into your life? You know, you can have a little dialog with this baby's spirit, like, 'Would you like to come live in my womb?' Why don't you try to connect with it? Because it's there."

So during one of my regular evening meditations, I gave it a try. I said, "Hi baby spirit. My womb is nice and cozy, and I'm inviting you to come in, little being of light." Doing that meditation helped me let go of all the over-thinking and worry. It's funny, because people would say, "As soon as you let go, that's when things happen." Two or three months later, I was pregnant. I found out December 19, which was very close to the deadline I had set.

The breast cancer diagnosis was devastating, but it gave me the courage to make some positive changes in my life. I might not have changed my lifestyle—treating my body better and eating healthier—and this made me so thankful toward the baby. I still have to monitor, with regular ultrasound scanning of my breasts, but everything was clear when I was pregnant. Looking back, I feel like my baby was protecting me and supporting my health.

Our Reflection on Elizabeth's Story

Elizabeth talked about the idea of surrender, which is a core tenet of various strains of contemplative faith and spirituality. In *The Wisdom Way of Knowing*, Rev. Cynthia Borgeault writes that surrender is not to be confused with "'rolling over and playing dead.' On the contrary, interior surrender is often precisely what makes it possible to see a decisive action that must be taken and to do it with courage and strength."[29] Tosha Silver also writes extensively about the idea of spiritual surrender; her books include prayers to help us surrender and go with the flow, such as:

> *Allow me, Divine, to willingly embrace and move with Your divine flow, knowing every true need is always met. May I know all unfolds in the right timing, may I trust all delays work only for my highest good.*[30]

Michael Singer also writes about these ideas in a more analytical manner that seeks to teach us that we are not just our thoughts and emotions. In *The Untethered Mind*, he described the unruly, unsettled mind as The Roommate—and a very unpleasant roommate at that. The idea of surrender is also related to acceptance, which we discuss in Chapter 13, and mindfulness, which is one of our coping techniques.

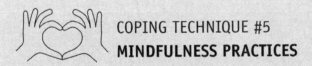 ## COPING TECHNIQUE #5
MINDFULNESS PRACTICES

Elizabeth described using meditation and qigong to cope with the stress of breast cancer and trying to conceive. At the root, these practices seek to build mindfulness. One simple definition of mindfulness is "moment to moment awareness."[31] It involves observing your thoughts, feelings, and physical sensations without creating a storyline or judgment. So often we try to reduce our suffering by changing our external environment. However, no matter how hard we work at that, stress remains. Here's a typical scenario: We wake up and are desperate to get to the coffee pot. That first cup is a salve, but by 8 a.m. we are in the car irritated with traffic. We then may feel good once we arrive at work and delve into a project, but then an annoying co-worker distracts us. The list goes on and on. We feel good temporarily, but are never truly satisfied. This is because a real sense of contentment comes only from within. That is what mindfulness is all about. It stops us from reacting and helps create an internal peaceful space. This is different from happiness.

Mindfulness can be developed by formal meditation as well as informal practices. It begins by learning to observe our feelings, thoughts, and body without judging them as good or bad and without forcing any negative thoughts or feelings to go away. We spend a lot of time trying to avoid negative experiences while we chase down pleasurable ones. The problem with this is that it never truly works. We may be able to achieve some temporary happiness, but ultimately those negative feelings and thoughts creep back in.

Mindfulness involves embracing our thoughts, feelings, and experiences. All of them. We need to be patient with the process. So often we try a new practice and get angry with ourselves because it is not working. Our mind is still judging, wandering, agitated. Developing mindfulness is like building muscles. No one can go from being a couch potato to running a marathon without a lot of training. Understanding that, and developing patience toward yourself and the process, will help you achieve your goals.

It is also important to understand that the goal-oriented attitude that may be helpful in other aspects of life is detrimental to developing mindfulness. Yes, we have a goal of becoming more mindful, which will help us be less reactive. However, to focus on this is contrary to the practice itself. Approaching a mindfulness practice with set expectations will only cause more stress. You must adopt a playful, experimental approach. This creates less of a struggle and helps us reach our goal more readily.

The next time you are feeling tense, angry, or disappointed, try staying with the feeling by observing it like a detached scientist. Observe your physical state: are your muscles tight, jaw clenched, shoulders hunched, heart beating faster? Notice all of these sensations while resisting the temptation to label them as good or bad. When your mind starts to add a storyline to it (i.e., "I'm so upset my period came; I'll never get pregnant. It's so unfair!"), direct your mind back to the feeling: "I'm upset." You may literally need to firmly and kindly say to yourself, "I'm stopping this story line! It is important not to judge my feelings." Although there is great benefit to challenging your thoughts and widening your view, that is not mindfulness. Be sure to observe your physical state since that is often the first sign of stress.

More on Mindfulness

For information on meditation centers and books that can help you further explore mindfulness, check out:

• **kadampa.org**

• *How to Solve Our Human Problems: The Four Noble Truths* by Geshe Kelsang Gyatso (Glen Spey, NY: Tharpa Publicaiton, 2007).

• *Introduction to Buddhism: An Explanation of the Buddhist Way of Life* by Geshe Kelsang Gyatso (Glen Spey, NY: Tharpa Publications, 2008).

How to Meditate

Formal meditation is a great way to build mindfulness. Meditation is not a "blank mind." It is a mind focused on a specific object. In the meditation classes that Sharon teaches, she recommends using your breath as that object as it is neutral and you always have it. Below are some simple steps to get started:

• Find a comfortable spot to sit. This can be in a chair or on a cushion on the floor. The important thing is that your back is straight.

• Place your hands comfortably on your lap.

• Place your tongue gently behind your upper teeth. This will help keep your jaw relaxed.

• Set a timer. It doesn't matter how long you start with, anywhere between 5 and 20 minutes is good.

• Close your eyes gently and focus on your breath. As thoughts come in to your mind, let them pass just like birds flying in the sky. You can notice them, but don't follow them.

• Keep going back to observing your breath. Don't change how you are breathing, just observe it.

A daily meditation practice will make being mindful easier and more spontaneous. (Please see sidebar on how to meditate.) It is important to understand that it is completely natural for your mind to wander during meditation. Sharon has been meditating for almost two decades and still has trouble with it many days. You can also build mindfulness with some more informal practices. Take a mundane activity like washing the dishes. The next time you are at the sink, really pay attention to the water, soap, feel of the dish, and scrubbing action. Focus on those sensations instead of your typical mind wanderings and see how you feel afterwards.

Developing mindfulness is the basis of future work. Just like you need to build a foundation before you build a house, you need to create a calmer, clearer mind before you can embrace new ways of viewing your situation and learning coping techniques. Just like endurance and strength improve every time you work out, your ability to be mindful improves every time you practice it. Therefore, aim for at least five minutes a day. However, the longer and more frequently you practice, the better.

We cannot control when we will conceive or if we encounter major health issues along the way. We can only control our response.

We cannot control when we will conceive or if we encounter major health issues along the way, as Elizabeth did in the above narrative. We can only control our response. In order to respond to life's challenges in a productive manner, we need to change internally. Mindfulness is a method to do that. Fertility journeys are often long and painful. We can actively work to change our relationship to our thoughts so that we generate different, healthier responses.

In Due Time

Managing Your Mind While Waiting for Baby

No matter how long or short, difficult or easy, the road to motherhood can be daunting. This chapter offers more information on stress and coping, including healthy stress. A friend of ours once described trying to conceive as "a bit rollercoaster-y," and the stories in this book demonstrate that many women experience ups and downs on the path to motherhood. No matter how long we have dreamed about having a baby or how prepared we are, many of us start to feel a little nervous when the process begins. It doesn't seem to matter if we have always wanted to be a mom or if we made the choice later in life. Most feel some nervous apprehension. Some of us are a little hesitant having sex without birth control for the first time. Some of us panic about what pregnancy and labor will actually be like.

If you are starting to mourn the loss of your freedom, or doubt your ability to give constantly or to have endless patience, this is normal and healthy. You are attempting to create a human being, which, in itself, is an awe-inspiring proposition. Pregnancy and labor carry their own hosts of anxieties. Then, you will be charged with raising said human being into a productive, well-adjusted adult. Your life will never be the same—which is thought-provoking and sometimes cause for a sleepless night.

You may be way past theses anxious thoughts and say, "Bring it on. I've been waiting long enough and can't wait to get up at 2 a.m. to nurse!" Very well, then, because this is an example of healthy stress. Healthy stress activates you, forces you to prepare, and propels you into action. Healthy stress is why we have survived as a species for so long; we ran from the tigers and worried about storing harvests for the winter. It's also responsible for a lot of the success in life, such as getting through school or an important work presentation. The healthy stress of wanting to conceive a baby can drive you to take care of yourself and create an optimal environment for your fetus, just as Charlotte and Elizabeth described in previous chapters. It may also lead you to a fertility specialist if you do not conceive in a reasonable amount of time.

The problem arises when we are always feeling stressed. How does stress break you down? When you encounter a stressful situation (stuck in traffic, work demands, IVF cycle, being chased by a large animal, etc.) your body sets off its emergency response system located in your brain's hypothalamus. The hypothalamus rounds up its sergeant, your adrenal glands, to release the foot soldiers cortisol and adrenaline. These and other hormones, along with nerve signals, prepare the body for action.

This is otherwise known as flight or fight. Your heart rate, respiration, and blood pressure increase as extra glucose is released in the bloodstream and your muscles tense. Nonessential functions like digestion, immune response, and reproductive functioning are slowed down so the body can direct all its attention to survival. This is why some women stop ovulating or have delayed ovulation when stressed.

Prolonged amounts of cortisol are associated with excess abdominal fat, which may alter fertility. Even if it doesn't, it's still annoying and unhealthy for you in the long run. Chronic stress response can cause fatigue, difficulty sleeping, poor concentration, anxiety, depression, and frequent infections.

Anxiety is a little bit different than stress in that it is a pervasive sense of worry, not necessarily triggered by any one event. It is closely related to stress, though. Often the two are intertwined. Increased stress can trigger anxiety. It is important to understand that many people who suffer from anxiety, don't necessarily identify it as such. They simply feel tight or stop enjoying themselves. They may feel the weight of the world on them. Often times, Sharon's patients voice their fears, complaining that they always think the worst is going to happen. That's anxiety. Anxiety and stress are tightly interwoven. Some people have a genetic predisposition to anxiety, whereas others develop it in response to a situation. Regardless, it warrants treatment.

Being affected by stress is not a personal weakness. It happens to everyone. It is actually a strong and insightful person who recognizes how stress is affecting them and seeks help.

Someone struggling with constant stress will feel on edge, irritable, and fatigued. She may have digestive issues, insomnia, and intrusive thoughts that constantly replay in her head. She may find it impossible to relax and enjoy the moment, and frequently feels less pleasure in life.

When we feel stress, it's often over things we can't control. Think about the last time you were stuck in traffic, desperate to get to your destination, thinking, "Why can't these people just move?" You have no power to control the other cars, nor the obstacles preventing them from moving, but you may feel your jaw tighten as you clench the wheel. Now you have two problems: you are stuck in traffic and you feel badly. Sometimes you develop a third problem: feeling bad about yourself because of how you responded to the stressor. For example, if your spouse calls you on the phone while you're stuck in traffic, you might respond brusquely, and then afterwards you may find fault with yourself for being snippy. You can't control the traffic, but you can control your responses to it, and that principle can be applied to your fertility journey as well.

Before we continue, we want to clarify that being affected by stress is not a personal weakness. It happens to everyone. It is actually a strong and insightful person who recognizes how stress is affecting them and seeks help. If you are having trouble conceiving, it may or may not be due to stress. Fertility is a wildly complicated multifactorial process. For some women, stress may interfere with conception. Difficulty conceiving may also cause a detrimental level of stress that can interfere with truly enjoying life. Many normal human beings would experience that level of stress in the same situation. We will never offer the advice, "Just relax, and it will happen." However, since prolonged stress does affect your health, emotions, relationships, and general functioning, it is important to manage it. Below we share a brief primer on cognitive behavioral therapy, a good option for managing stress and anxiety.

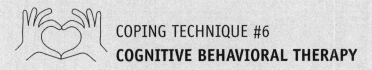

COPING TECHNIQUE #6
COGNITIVE BEHAVIORAL THERAPY

Cognitive behavioral therapy (CBT) employs the connection between events, thoughts, feelings, and behavior to empower people and ease their suffering. The heart of CBT is understanding the core beliefs learned in childhood that drive the thoughts you are having today. It offers a method to change your response to questions like these:

• What types of running commentary does your mind generate and how does it make you feel?

• How do you feel when you hear fear-mongering statistics?

• How do you feel when you read well-researched reassuring articles?

Note: This is not always easy to do, which is why we recommend working with a therapist if you're faced with deep or painful emotions and feelings that you can't make sense of.

Women over 35 who are trying to get pregnant are subjected to all sorts of negative input both externally and internally. You may have your own insecurities about your fertility and, unfortunately, they can be easily reinforced by the media, friends, and family. The good news is that you possess some power to change this. You can change your feelings by controlling the language you allow in.

In the simplest terms, CBT works as follows: Your period arrives (**event**) and you have a **thought** such as, "I'll never get pregnant!" This makes you **feel** hopeless and sad, which leads to sitting on the sofa all weekend instead of going out with friends (**behavior**), which then leaves you **feeling** isolated and lonely. It's a vicious cycle.

Take a moment to think about this in your own life. Now apply this to your fertility journey. What actions are you taking, and what thoughts are you having? What makes you feel good? What leads to hopelessness? If you carefully examine this, you'll find you have a lot more control than you previously thought.

Liberating, isn't it? The first step is to have accurate information. For example, no matter what you have been told, the average woman's chances of conceiving over 35 are quite good. Second, surround yourself with positive people. Be explicitly clear that you are only accepting encouragement and hope. Seek out women who have had their first baby over 35 and, if appropriate, talk to them about it. When doubts start to seep in, remember these women.

The goal is not to stop thoughts or feelings; it is to change them. You can entertain two ideas at once. If you have a thought like, "I shouldn't have waited this long; it will never happen," you can also think, "Sally is pregnant with her third, and she is 41." Counteracting negative thoughts with positive ones will lead to lighter feelings. Lighter feelings will lead to more positive thoughts, which will lead to more helpful behaviors.

The goal is not to stop thoughts or feelings; it is to change them. You can entertain two ideas at once.

If the entire approach to starting a family has left you feeling stressed and bewildered, try changing your language around it. One of our blog readers writes beautifully of her experience:

My husband and I have been trying for three months, and we have both felt a lot of pressure. My friends who are moms recommended all of these fertility tracking methods before we started trying. I have been monitoring my temp, checking my cervical mucous, and using LH (luteinizing hormone) test strips. I have to say, these techniques are all very interesting and I have learned a lot about my fertility. However, we have also felt a lot of pressure to time sex perfectly and this has taken the romance out of the experience for us. In retrospect, I think we could have started out just making love often without protection for a few months before using all the ovulation prediction methods. A wise friend of mine also recommended not using the phrase "trying to conceive," and instead saying "allowing myself to conceive." Sometimes, we just have to get out of our own way.

Dissecting this from a CBT viewpoint, the thought that they were "trying to conceive" led to the behavior of timing sex perfectly, which led to feelings of stress. It is imperative that you are mindful of the words you use when talking to yourself and others. If "trying to conceive" makes you feel stressed, then change it to something more joyful. This reader preferred to "allow" it to happen. Perhaps their results would have been the same either way, but they would have felt better if they approached it differently. We chose to share this example because this couple was trying for only three months and has no known fertility issues. The stress of *trying* to conceive can affect couples regardless of the length or details of their journey.

You may not always feel great when leaving therapy. The important thing is that you are feeling growth.

If your age feels old to you then don't think of yourself in number of years. In fact, only place one candle on your next birthday cake. If you despair every time your period comes, then add to your inner dialogue: "There is hope that I can be pregnant next month."

The above is a very short and abbreviated approach of CBT. True CBT involves examining the core beliefs that underlie your thoughts and feelings. It should be done with a qualified therapist. If you find that you are spending more time than not feeling disinterested, fatigued, restless, tight, tense, irritable, or are simply not enjoying life, then please consider seeking professional counseling. Therapy (counseling) can be short- or long-term. Call your insurance company or look on the *Psychology Today* website for a list of therapists in your area, and find out who accepts your insurance. If you are being seen at a fertility center, they can often recommend one as well. Many therapists have websites that explain their counseling styles and what areas they specialize in. Ideally, you will find someone who understands fertility. However, that is not essential. A good therapist will follow your emotions and thoughts and doesn't necessarily need to understand the details.

Give the therapist five sessions. If, after the fifth session, you don't feel any type of change, then it may be time to either address the lack of progress with the therapist or simply look for a new one. Therapists are used to this. It does not mean that they are bad at their job; it simply means that they are not meeting your needs. You may not always feel great when leaving therapy. The important thing is that you are feeling growth.

The road to parenthood can be long or short, direct or circuitous. People respond to the journey in their own unique way. Our hope is that you will take care of yourself along the way. This is the best gift you can give yourself and your future child.

The Right Time

In this story, we meet Monica, whose feelings of uncertainty earlier in life changed to urgency later in life. Along the way, she received some ageist comments that she remembered well, even though she shared her experience with us almost two decades later. Early experiences limited Monica's desire for motherhood. For example, in 1978 she took a job in a neonatal intensive care unit.

Monica's Story

They didn't have the kind of technologies that they have now, so I saw many things that can go wrong in pregnancy. I think at that point I decided I'd never have kids. I just couldn't see going through a pregnancy worrying about everything that could go wrong. That was my whole perspective: having children meant having all these complicated things happen.

[Later her job involved teaching prenatal and childbirth classes and visiting new parents in their homes. She said, "So I knew a lot about babies—or so I thought." Like Erin, she got married in her twenties but it only lasted five years, ending in divorce.]

I don't think I was horribly worried about whether I would ever have children, but during the next five years or so I felt like I was running out of time. Plus my gynecologist kept urging me not to wait until after age 40 to start trying.

When my current husband and I were dating, we were pretty upfront about wanting children from the beginning. We are the same age, and neither of us had been ready for children until that point in our lives. My husband's brother was 50 when he had his first child, and my husband's dad had him when he was 50, so neither of us had the perspective that being older parents was unusual.

We got married in June of 1994. I got pregnant really quickly after we got married, which surprised me because I had never been pregnant in my whole life. I was still shocked and really nervous. So many things had changed.

No one ever said anything negative to us about being in our late thirties, and the people who knew us were very happy for us. The only thing that someone said once, which caught me off guard, was when a doctor, who was covering for my obstetrician, said, "Your abdomen looks just like a younger woman's." I thought I was a younger woman and had never thought of myself as being old.

It was a huge disappointment to lose that pregnancy. I had a blighted ovum, so there was never a heartbeat or a viable fetus. Although I was worried that my time was nearly up, I wanted to try again, because I knew I could get pregnant. I also kept thinking about what the gynecologist told me, that I may only have until age 40.

[At this point, Monica "became a bit of a scientist about conceiving" through fertility awareness and she became pregnant again within a few months.]

With my second pregnancy, I was more nervous because I was afraid I would miscarry again. At that point, I really wanted to get pregnant. I tried not to think about it so much and to go on with normal activities, but I worried about the health of my baby until the day she was born.

We wanted to have two kids. Getting pregnant was easier the second time, because I knew that I could have a baby. We were very fortunate that way. I had my son when I was 41. With both kids, it only took about three months of trying.

I love having kids at my age. I'm 58, am around teenagers all the time, and I find it energizing. I'm close to the mothers of my daughter's two best friends from middle and high school, and my son's best friend's mother. My age falls in the middle of all of us. Part of the older parent connection is because my husband and I are both working and we decided to put our kids in private schools. I would guess that the parents in private schools may be a little older because you have to be able to pay for it.

For me, I never felt like I was waiting to have children; it was just the way my life happened. I don't think it would have been the right time five or ten years earlier. Since our children have been in school, we've met so many different types of families, and we've seen kids from every part of the world that have come into families through adoption. There are lots of ways to have a family. Whenever it's the right time for people is when they can hopefully find the way to have a family.

Reflecting on Monica's Story

Although Monica's gynecologist may not have intended to give her a pregnancy deadline of age 40, that is how the comments were interpreted. And the gynecologist who told her that her abdomen looked like a younger woman's probably meant to give her a compliment, but the effect was to heighten her awareness of a stigma she hadn't previously considered. In his book *The MindBody Code: How to Change the Beliefs that Limit Your Health, Longevity, and Success*, Dr. Mario Martinez urges us against telling other people our age, because that frequently leads them to project negative expectations onto us. Yet, concealing our age from health care providers is not possible, since they already have access to that information. Tosha Silver (one of Emma's favorite spiritual teachers) says that when someone makes an ageist comment it is akin to having someone hand you a cup of poison. It is then your decision whether you are going to drink it. In other words, you have to decide whether you are going to internalize that message. We hope that at this point in the book it is clear that we do NOT want you to drink the poison.

How Hard to Try

After getting pregnant by luck and then having a miscarriage, Monica started trying to get pregnant again by monitoring signs of ovulation and timing sex accordingly. Although fertility is often beyond the bounds of conversation with acquaintances, people will sometime share that they are trying to get pregnant. But that could mean anything from not using birth to control to having in vitro fertilization. One friend of a friend claimed to have had sex with her husband every day for six months while trying to conceive. When her pregnancy test was positive, her husband supposedly said, "Can we stop having sex every day now?" It raised the question: How hard do you need to try?

Some national surveys have examined the frequency of sex among married and cohabitating couples, and how this changes over time, without looking at fertility intentions. These studies have suggested that married couples in their thirties and forties have intercourse less frequently than those in their twenties. This is, of course, a cliché in the popular culture. However, the differences found between older and younger couples do not seem large enough to affect fertility. For example, one study found that married people ages 25–29 had sex about ten times per month, compared with about eight times per month for those 35–44.[32]

More relevant are studies that included only couples that were trying to become pregnant. One Danish study enrolled women who were trying to conceive, were less than 40 years old, and without a history of infertility, and then maintained contact with them for one year or until they became pregnant, whichever was sooner.[33] Among women less than age 25, 31 percent had intercourse four or more times per week, compared with 21 percent of women ages 25–29 and 15 percent of women in their thirties. However, the study showed little influence of sexual frequency on the probability of getting pregnant.

Some researchers treating infertile couples have examined whether infertility leads to stress, depression, anxiety, viewing sex like a chore, or a combination of these factors, and, if so, whether this results in less frequent sex. This would then compound any physiological problems that reduced fertility. Several studies bear this out, to some extent. In one example, 25 percent of men seeking care at an infertility clinic reported having intercourse less than four times per month, while most men in the study reported having sex more than five times per month. Five or more times per month compares to the national average, but we think couples trying to get pregnant might want to be a bit above average in this regard.

Other studies have also suggested that infertility could be associated with male sexual difficulties, such as premature ejaculation and erectile dysfunction. The requirement to perform for infertility tests and treatments creates anxiety in many men. Men are not the only ones facing difficulties. Women experiencing infertility generally report less satisfaction with their sex lives, although this is not always found to be true. Surveys attempt to measure this by asking women about their satisfaction related to sexual desire, arousal, and orgasm and whether these issues cause them to feel distressed; some studies also assess pain during intercourse.

Surveys in the United States have found about 40 percent of women *overall* experience problems in one of these areas, regardless of whether they are trying to conceive, with desire being the most common area of dissatisfaction.[34] Again, not all studies find this association, and not everyone experiences this. If you are just starting the process of trying to conceive, do not worry that it is paradoxically going to ruin your sex life.

But wait, you may be thinking, are we concerned with frequency or *timing*? Timing sex to coincide with ovulation might seem like what people mean when they say they are trying to conceive. But not necessarily. For example, in the Danish study mentioned earlier, less than half of women ages 35–40 were using a method to improve their odds of timing intercourse to maximize their chance of conception, such as charting their basal body temperature, monitoring cervical mucus, or using a luteinizing hormone or ovulation test kit.[35] A smaller U.S.-based study of women trying to conceive found that only 6 percent of women checked their cervical mucus consistently, but those who did were twice as likely to get pregnant.[36]

If you are just starting the process of trying to conceive, do not worry that it is paradoxically going to ruin your sex life.

However, other research also suggests that couples often have trouble identifying when the fertile window occurs. One study—albeit one funded by a fertility monitor manufacturer—found that most women who started using a fertility monitor became pregnant within three cycles.[37] Based on this, the authors concluded that most of the couples had been previously mistiming intercourse, even though 84 percent said they had used some method of predicting ovulation.

Dr. Allen J. Wilcox, one of the epidemiologists to identify the six-day fertile window in the 1990s, points out this problem, noting that couples may easily miss the fertile window if they wait to have intercourse until they think they are in it.[38] We are also exposed to misleading conventional advice. Later Wilcox writes, "In only about 30 percent of women is the fertile window entirely within the days of the menstrual cycle identified by clinical guidelines—that is, between days 10 and 17. Most women reach their fertile window earlier and others much later."[39]

In his 2010 book *Fertility and Pregnancy: An Epidemiologic Perspective*, Wilcox says that one of the unanswered questions in reproductive epidemiology is, "How can women identify their fertile days?"[40] The problem, as he states it, is that once the signs of impending ovulation are noticeable, most days in the six-day fertile window have passed. The conventional wisdom is that if your cycle is regular, then most likely your fertile days are the same for every cycle. That is the potential benefit of basal body temperature charting. However, Wilcox argues against putting too much faith in this notion. So maybe trying by not trying too hard is a valid strategy. Another friend, trying to conceive at age 39, was advised by her doctor to make love every other day, rather than trying to predict the most fertile times. It worked! She had a healthy baby within a year. And then another one at age 44!

One of our friends described her approach to trying to conceive as "feeling the love in the air." That may be a valid strategy. In a 2004 study, Wilcox examined a group of women who were not trying to conceive and found that they were more likely to have intercourse during their fertile window.[41] A likely reason is that when follicle-stimulating hormone and luteinizing hormone surge to induce ovulation in women's bodies, testosterone levels also rise, leading to increased libido.[42] It also may be that male testosterone rises in response to ovulation response and that intercourse influences the timing of ovulation.[43] So do not be afraid to follow your instincts.

12 We Like Life

In this chapter, we share a conversation between Renee and Tracey, two women who are married to each other, about their experience getting pregnant. We enjoyed the back and forth exchange they had, so we kept the story in that format.

Tracey worked in computer programming after college and was in a serious relationship with another woman. She balked at having a baby with that partner, partly because she wanted to make a career change and worried that a baby would make that financially impossible. After that relationship ended, she starting dating Rene, who encouraged her to pursue her longstanding dream of becoming a lawyer. When Tracey was in law school, they began considering starting a family.

Renee and Tracey's Story

Rene: *It wasn't that I didn't want to have children before that; I did. I also saw it as a decision to not make lightly and certainly not something you would do accidentally. I was very thoughtful about it. It was something I wanted to do very deliberately, if I was going to do it.*

Tracey: *I always knew I was gay, since I could formulate thought. I had to connect that to the version of motherhood I saw. These two spheres, in my head, were so separate. Once I realized that being a wonderful mom didn't require long nails and dresses, I was eager to be one. My mom is pretty conservative,* *so there has been a transition period to get her accustomed to me being gay. When I came out to her, the first thing she said was, "But I want you to have kids."*

[Renee said she had always known that she would like to experience pregnancy and faced a crisis in her twenties when diagnosed with lupus and told that it might be impossible or unsafe for her to conceive. But by the time she Tracey were together a decade later, her health had stabilized, and she had completed her doctorate and felt that her career was on track. She felt that the time was right. Then, she said, "The universe intervened." She was hospitalized with complications resulting from the medication she had been taking for lupus. Her doctors decided to wean her off her medications, which was better for health in terms of trying to conceive. To further prepare her body, she drank little alcohol and tried her best to reduce her coffee intake.]

Rene: *I decided to do what I could to be as healthy as possible, but realized that drastic changes in my life would make me crazy. I needed to live life as normally as possible with a few changes to just make sure I was as healthy as possible. Other than that, we started the fertility testing —the basic package, follicle counts, blood work, regular menses and ovulation. Even though we got a clean bill of health from all of the fertility docs to try, we still thought it would take at least a year. So we started with the assumption that we wouldn't have a baby until Tracey was out of law school. We thought, even if I am able to conceive, maybe I won't carry to term. We assumed the worst of all.*

Finally being with the right partner was huge, because I had watched two generations of women raise kids by themselves. I would not have had a child on my own. Hats off to single moms! I support them. It is a really hard way to live your life. Being in the right marriage, feeling good about where we were and the decision we were making—and that we could individually and collectively support a child—was critical. We were fortunate to be able to plan it all.

Tracey: *Because we were exposed to divorce growing up, Renee and I knew that we didn't want that, and I think that is why you see women of our generation holding off to get married, or choosing not to get married and holding off on kids until they are sure of their marriage. I don't think the generation before us felt they had that option. They had more pressure.*

THE FERTILITY CENTER

Tracey: *I felt so tangential to the conception process, just by the way that it is set up. We caused an occasional kink in the fertility clinic's wheel by being gay, rather than having problems conceiving. Their forms are made for a male and a female. Not having appropriate forms for a same-sex couple was frustrating.*

Rene: *I think for me it was a challenge because I'm used to navigating the medical community from a problem standpoint, and I was finally going in without an actual problem, and I was still problematized. I wasn't excited to be there. I was a little hostile about it even though I really wanted the baby.*

Tracey: *I chose the sperm. That was the one thing I latched onto. I don't have sperm; I'm going to get the sperm. It seemed like all of the donors from one clinic were assholes. You're reading the profiles, and you are like, "Are you serious?" For example, "I'm a doctor, and I think it's my responsibility to share my genetic background." Um, delete!*

For one sperm bank, they give you a selection of information about the donors, including essays they write. One such question is: What kind of animal would you be? We had about fifty of them, and I was getting more and more frustrated, because if I read about another horse, stag, or lion, I was going to go ballistic. I was at my wit's end, and read one that said, "I'd be a seahorse." I'm like "What the..." First of all, it's not an animal, and second of all, what does it mean? What are you saying about yourself that you would be a seahorse?

Rene: *That was a breaking point. We were in the kitchen, and she just lost it.*

Tracey: *Renee was great about it, she was like [in a placating tone], "We don't have to have a seahorse sperm." And I'm like, "Good, because no kid of mine will come from a seahorse."*

Finally, I came back to the list, and I found the guy. He answered the clinic's dumb questions by writing out all of the lyrics for his favorite Talking Heads songs. He did a doodle of faces. They left him alone in a room, and he did what he wanted to do, which is exactly what I would have done. He is mechanically minded, which I am as well. He loves to tinker. He had what I wanted to merge with her genetic material.

Rene: *Another important criterion was that the potential dad was willing to be contacted when the child turns 18. If that was something that our child wanted in life, we wanted to give her that option.*

We did intrauterine insemination, a bizarre six-minute process. You go in, you lie down, and the doctor does the insemination. You lie on your back for five minutes, and you walk out.

Tracey: *I was there for each time. It was psychologically hard. I felt out of my element. One part that I found disconcerting was that the people at the clinic spent a lot of time covering their own bases. For example, when the nurse and the doctor come into the room with the vial of sperm, they make a point of showing the number of the sperm donor. This made me anxious, because we have no idea whether that sperm is the sperm. You have a sheet that says that it is, but what if it is the wrong sperm?*

We were going through this thing, and it was profound, and Renee was putting all of this pressure on herself. I very much viewed the whole process to be all about her. What does she need? What can help her? I found myself in a supportive role. A lot of the times, there is nothing I could do. She just needed me to

Staying Connected

It is common for couples to feel disconnected when going through IVF. Jodilyn Owen, midwife and author of *The
Essential Homebirth Guide,* recommends that couples try to
have an orgasm together before IVF treatments, because it
brings an oxytocin burst that promotes a feeling of con-
nectedness and leads to a more positive association with
the experience.

be still. That was hard, because I'm a fixer.

Rene: *After the first time, we went to the beach. I had a lot of
cramping, and I knew it wasn't right. The second time I was in
the middle of some crazy work stuff, so I don't remember. The
third time I was able to take the rest of the day off. Before you
know it has worked and you're just in the "trying" stage, it's gut
wrenching. Each time you have a failure, you have to sit with it
emotionally to come to terms that you might not conceive. That
is incredibly hard on a partner who wants to fix everything, because how can you possibly fix that? I couldn't even tell her what
I needed.*

Tracey: *Couple that with the "static" women give other wom-
en. I was struck by the amount of opinions, critiques, and recommendations from other women about getting pregnant.
When Renee mentioned she was trying, some would talk about
how they got pregnant so quickly, or they went the other way
and talked about how horrible it was. She rarely found someone
willing to let her be without imposing their experience or suggestions on her.*

*My younger sister was a huge support. She already had a
baby and was due with the second when Lucy came, so it was
cool to share that. She has given me so much wisdom, which I*

didn't expect from a younger sister.

Rene: *She was the only one who consistently said, "You need to do what feels right for you." She was always validating our decisions. There are very few people in this process that give you a blank check.*

In truth, some of it is projection. You feel this judgment on yourself. I had put childbearing on hold. I was selfish, I got a master's degree, a PhD, pursued my career, and now I want to have kids, so maybe it serves me right if I can't get pregnant. Again, none of that came from other people. It was all my projection.

Add to that being a lesbian. All of a sudden, all of these really ugly voices that you didn't even realize were in your mind decide to speak up. It's a gross space. Even if you can intellectually challenge it point by point, it still brings up deep feelings of inadequacy.

It was probably the first time in our relationship that we fought. There is all of this pressure around the insemination. Often, this has to do with the weird timing around when you ovulate, how quickly you call the center, and if they call you back on time. At times I felt bitter that we were held hostage by the process, whereas other people get drunk on a Saturday night and figure out two months later that they made a baby. And we didn't even have it nearly as bad as other people do. Some people's children are years in the making. You play that narrative in your head as well.

The third time they did the insemination, I had this sense of peace. I said to Tracey, "I hate to jinx this, but if they tell me in two weeks that I'm pregnant, I won't be surprised at all."

Tracey: *She came running in one morning exclaiming, "I'm pregnant!" The first thing I thought was, "Wow, she's pregnant," and the second thought was, "Oh crap, her due date will be right at exam time." The whole thing was just hilarious. I had to talk to my university, which has the word "Catholic" in its* name, about moving the exam because you need a really good reason to move one. So I sat down with the administrator and she asked, "What can I help you with?"

I said, "Well, my partner is having our first child and the due date is on one of my exams."

She leaned back in her chair, put her glasses down and said, "Well, we like life."

And I said, "We do, too."

THE PREGNANCY AND BIRTH

Rene: *Everybody asks you, "Did you stop drinking coffee?" I did not stop drinking coffee because nobody should be around me if I'm not drinking coffee! I had a cup of coffee every morning. Exercise was something I would not give up either, partly for my sanity, but mostly for her well-being.*

[During Rene's pregnancy, people would occasionally make comments like, "Oh, are you really OK to do that?" She was shocked by how many people told her their delivery horror stories. Meanwhile, her job related to reducing infant mortality, so she had a lot of access to information—probably too much. Plus, she was categorized as high risk because of her age and lupus, and this resulted in her having what she called a "traditional obstetrics practice" rather than the midwifery practice she would have preferred. Her obstetrician wanted to induce labor at thirty-nine weeks' gestation, but she was able to convince the doctor to wait until she was forty weeks. Nonetheless, her labor was induced, and then after fifty hours resulted in a C-section.]

Tracey: *My mom and brother were there the night Lucy was born. My mother said, "She is so beautiful, and I can say that objectively because we are not genetically related."*

Rene: *I feel so blessed to have physically been able to get through a pregnancy. OK, I gained forty-five pounds, there* *were pieces that were very tough, but for the most part I really loved it. I loved that I got glimpses of her personality before she was born. When we have baby no. 2, we will use Tracey's egg and the same donor, but I'll carry with the second. Because she won't be a genetic link to me, I would love to have that tie to her, of carrying her. Hopefully, I will be lucky enough to be able to.*

Tracey: *If not, I will be willing to try it. It will be the toughest thing for both of us, tougher than law school, because I am not going to be easy. I never felt the maternal instinct to be pregnant. I said, "I'll be the B womb." Then I saw her go through it and was like, "I'm really glad you can do it because I ain't doing that!" My mother is dumbfounded that Renee would take that on for me.*

Rene: *Love.*

More Thoughts on Timing

I think you get it right in your thirties; I think you finally hit your stride in your thirties. In my prior relationship, my ex wanted to have kids. I knew that wasn't right, I wasn't ready yet. Looking back, it was so clear. I realized things needed to change, and I needed to do something to get myself to that point. That is what older people understand. You should be confident in that you know what you need to do to become who you are, and in a lot of cases what you have already done. Take confidence in that, and put it toward this new process you are embarking on. Know you have gotten yourself to the point where you are alright. You succeeded, you're good, go with it. Surround yourself with the knowledge of that. You have gotten yourself right, and you can get the tools to get this right.

–Tracey

Our Reflection on Renee and Tracey's Story

Tracy and Renee illustrate how fluid our attitudes toward motherhood can be and the importance of waiting until the time feels right. They wanted a stable marriage and established careers. They wanted to come into themselves before committing to children. Their approach was thoughtful and wise, and they communicated openly. Yet, like all of us, they occasionally found that external factors sometimes exposed insecurities. For example, Tracy talked about how other women pressed their views on her. Renee talked about the "ugly voices" that arose. Although some of these situations are inevitable, it is helpful to think about how to minimize them.

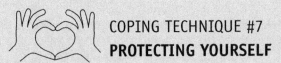 COPING TECHNIQUE #7
PROTECTING YOURSELF

Women often say that they never noticed how many people are pregnant or have young babies until they start trying for one of their own. We home in on the things that interest us, so it's natural to notice more big bellies at this time. This can cause some painful situations. Even if you haven't been trying for very long, jealousy can arise around others' pregnancies. Once pregnant, fear and anxiety can be worsened by others' horror tales.

Pregnancy and childbirth are, perhaps, the two most epic events in our lives. This is why so many women like to connect over them. It can be a driver for wanting to share stories and information. That being said, it is OK to create some space between other women's pregnancies and yourself. You may need to block a friend's Facebook newsfeeds (she won't know you are doing it) or avoid certain pregnant co-workers. It's not about hurting or isolating others; it's about protecting yourself. It is also fine to avoid sharing information about your own fertility experiences with others.

MORE ON PREGTIQUETTE

In Chapter 2, we introduced the idea of pregtiquette, or how to manage all of the icky emotional and interpersonal situations that can arise while trying to conceive or during pregnancy. We have inserted pregtiquette examples throughout the book. We talked about nosey questions related to fertility and how to handle fertility-related scheduling conflicts. Renee and Tracey talked about the unsolicited advice and alarming stories they were told. Below are some ideas on how to handle these common scenarios.

Scenario 1: You announce your pregnancy and immediately your co-worker delves into how horrible her delivery was.

Response: It is OK to interrupt her, just make it about you as opposed to her. For example, "Ooh, I'm sorry, but I am going to stop you because I have such high anxiety, I really can't hear others' birth stories right now. I'm sorry, I know it's important to you, but I'm just not up for it."

Scenario 2: You plan on an unmediated birth (no epidural) and your sister tells you that is ridiculous and you will never be able to manage the pain.

Response Option 1: "Um, I'm pretty sure women have been doing it for several thousand years." OK, that might be a bit snarky, so check out Option 2.

Response Option 2: "I appreciate your concern. I know it may be tough, which is why we are preparing for it." If she persists, then politely tell her you really need encouragement right now and if she can't offer that then you're not open to discussing it.

Scenario 3: You plan on using a midwife or having a home-birth. Your friend tells you that it is totally irresponsible and unsafe.

Response Option 1: This is, unfortunately, fairly common. Many people don't know that a midwife is a highly educated health professional and that homebirths are only offered to women who are considered low risk. You can take the time to educate people on this. However, if that feels too taxing, check out Option 2.

Response Option 2 "I appreciate your concern. Believe me, no one is more invested in a healthy outcome than me. I'm making the best decisions for the baby and me based on sound research."

Prejudice about where to deliver can go both ways. Not only do some take issue with using a midwife or birthing at home, in some social circles the idea of delivering in a hospital or with a doctor is automatically met with the presumption that it will be full of interventions and overly "medicalized." Sharon had a beautiful all-natural hospital birth with a midwife, sipping tea, lights dim, and James Taylor playing.

Tracy also talked about how hard it was to support Renee emotionally during their IUIs. Renee spoke about fluctuating emotions and needing stillness. How we respond and what we need are so individualized that no other human could ever automatically meet that need. Expecting others to know exactly what you need is neither realistic nor fair. Being clear with others, setting boundaries, and developing your own internal resolves will help reduce tensions during this time of transition. These responses have all tended toward disclosing less, and that's probably a reflection of our personalities. We have met people who were quite open about their fertility journeys. Whatever works for you is the best option.

13 All the Time in the World

This narrative features Sarah, whose attitudes toward marriage and motherhood evolved throughout her life in one way, but in another sense it seems like she had certain core values that guided her. In some ways she's traditional and in some ways she's not. Her pregnancies are typical and they are not. In the midst of these contradictions, acceptance prevails as a common theme.

Sarah's Story

After having three children in her twenties, my mom had me at age 40 and my sister at age 43. She had gotten pregnant unexpectedly at 37, and the baby contracted meningitis and died when he was only one month old. My parents were devastated. Because they had been so happy about having another baby, they decided to try again for another child, after taking a couple of years to grieve.

My mother often told me that the best time of her life was when my sister and I were younger and that she enjoyed every second of raising us. She was more calm and focused and less selfish than she had been with my older siblings. It was the 1970s, and it seemed that practically no one else had babies at her age. In college, some people assumed she was my grandmother, but I didn't care because I didn't think they had as good of a mom as I had.

When I was 37 or 38, I got drunk and proposed to my boyfriend of ten years, telling him I wanted to have a baby. I think it was a hormonal thing that kicked in. We were already living together in a house that we owned, but had not felt the need to marry. Around that time we had started talking about marriage, because my boyfriend's brother had gotten engaged to a woman just four weeks after meeting her. At the last minute, she backed out. Since the plans had already been made, we considered taking their place. We didn't end up doing that; his mother had taken out insurance so that she wouldn't lose a dime if something happened. After my spontaneous proposal, we waited a year before getting married. Then I wanted to take a year to just enjoy being married before trying to conceive. Although I had not thought marriage would be important, it felt great, like another level of commitment. Basically, I was 39 and acted like I had all the time in the world.

I got through the hormone shots and the medical procedures, because I was willing to do whatever I had to do. I just accepted it as what was.

I never would have had children without being married. I'm traditional in that way. I think children need the stability of marriage. In fact, around the time I started contemplating having a family, a friend talked to me about getting pregnant with her boyfriend. I urged her to get married so she could give her child that sense of security, and they did.

After six months of trying to conceive, my husband and I went to a fertility doctor. We moved on to IVF pretty quickly. I am a pretty positive person and thought it would work the first time, so I was devastated when it didn't. During that phase of trying and waiting, I second guessed my decision to wait so long. But my husband told me that it wasn't meant to happen earlier, and I know he was right.

I got through the hormone shots and the medical procedures, because I was willing to do whatever I had to do. I just accepted it as what was. Sometimes life is not clean and neat. My best friend since high school, Ella, went through menopause at age 18, so she always knew that she would need fertility treatments. We were trying to conceive at the same time, so we went through it together. Sometimes I gave her hormone injections when her husband was out of town. (She ended up having twins.)

During this time, I was very conscientious about not reading anything negative, especially anything about women who couldn't conceive.

The second IVF worked. Soon after I got pregnant, I met Ella for coffee. I told her right away that I was pregnant. It turned out she was also pregnant, too, and was reluctant to tell me since I was going through fertility treatments. We had our sons within one month of each other.

Grief and Other Unsettling Emotions

Sarah and her friend were lucky to become pregnant at the same time. For other women, fertility issues can cause rifts in friendship. One of the hardest things about a fertility journey, especially a challenging and long one, is that it can bring out ugly emotions. Jealousy, anger, grief, and fear are all very common, and they can take us by surprise.

A note about grief from Sharon: *During the three years we were trying to conceive and then even after our beautiful girl was born, one thing I came to accept was a sense of loss. Our joy was accompanied by so much pain. I grieved 'what should have been,' meaning conceiving without all sorts of interventions and within a timely manner. We need to understand our emotions to better cope with them. It also helped me understand why, even after I gave birth, I still sometimes had odd reactions to other people's pregnancies. It wasn't jealously, it was grief. A friend compared it to getting married after her father had died. She didn't begrudge other people having their parents at their wedding, but whenever she went to a wedding she felt a twinge of sadness because her father was not able to walk her down the aisle.*

Pregnancy was great. I never had morning sickness. However, I continued to have high blood pressure, as I have throughout my adult life. At my thirty-seven-week prenatal check-up, my blood pressure was in the range of preeclampsia. The doctor said that I would have to stay in the hospital for monitoring, and if my blood pressure did not reduce in a few hours, they would have to induce labor. I was unhappy because I really wanted to go to Target and return some stuff that I had received at my baby shower the week before. I called my husband and said, "They won't let me go to Target." He was packing my bag for the hospital as I spoke, because he knew it was time.

Before they started my Pitocin drip (which is part of inducing labor), I stood up to go to the bathroom, and my water broke. I felt confused at first and did not understand what had happened, which is funny to think about in retrospect. After the nurse explained it to me, I accepted that it was time. My labor was pretty mild overnight. In the morning, they increased the Pitocin, and it became stronger. I was shaking between contractions; no one had told me that could happen. Then suddenly I had the urge to push, and in five or six pushes, he was out. The cord was wrapped around his neck loosely, and it slipped off easily. For that reason, they kept him in the NICU for a few days, but he was fine, just a bit tiny at four pounds, ten ounces.

I returned to work as a freelance Web designer less than two weeks later. I worked from home, and the baby just slept and nursed all the time, so I wanted something to occupy my time. I would prop the baby on a pillow to nurse or sleep, which left my hands free to work on the computer.

TRYING FOR A SECOND

When my son was about eighteen months old, we stopped using birth control. Neither of us wanted him to be an only child. I am one of five children and could not imagine growing up without siblings. In addition to having companions growing up, we didn't want him to have the sole responsibility of taking care of us when we were older.

We tried to conceive using frozen embryos from the previous fertility treatments, but I didn't conceive. A few months later, though, I suspected I was pregnant and went to my fertility doctor to be tested. Then I left for vacation in Puerto Rico. I was at Isabela Beach when the doctor's office called me to confirm. I thought the name Isabella would be perfect if I was having a girl, and had a feeling that the baby would be a girl.

When I got home, I went for an ultrasound. The technician said, "There's a really strong heartbeat—and there's a faint one." She had to call the doctor into the room. They warned me about the vanishing twin syndrome (when only one baby survives to birth), and so the idea of having twins felt tentative from the start. When I went back in a few weeks, both heartbeats were still there, and they could tell they were going to be identical twins.

I had another normal pregnancy and birth. The first year was not as easy as with my first baby; everyone says that the first year with twins is hard. The hardest part was being touched constantly. No one had warned me about that. I remember using a huge wraparound pillow to nurse both of the twins at the same time. After the twins were finished nursing, my older son would want to cuddle with me. Then, when he got up, the cat would jump into my lap. And when I went to bed, my husband wanted to be close physically.

It was so hard getting in and out of the house that we just did not go out as much as we had with only one baby. My husband felt like we never got a break, because each of us was holding one of them all of the time. Once they were old enough, I put them in preschool, and they really liked it. Now they are five and play together so well that in some ways having twins is easier than having one child. They don't know why identical twins occur; it's like one group of cells decides to break free and become *a separate person. I'm so glad my little one had the oomph to do that.*

It's still astounding to us that we have three children. In some ways, we miss our old lives, being able to go out whenever we wanted. At the same time, in many ways our life is the same as it was before we had children. We still live in the same house in the same city and pursue the same careers. For me, it was meant to be this way.

I have a great aunt whose mother had her at age 48, and a great-grandmother whose mother had her at 49. Now I'm 48, and every year at my annual check-up my ob-gyn warns me that I could still get pregnant. I have friends who are trying for their fourth child, but I don't have a desire for any more. Having children was an itch I had to scratch, and now I feel satisfied.

Our Reflection on Sarah's Story

We love the understated wisdom in this sentence: "I got through the hormone shots and the medical procedures because I was willing to do whatever I had to do. I just accepted it as what was. Sometimes life is not clean and neat."

One of the common reasons women feel shocked, surprised, and angered at their failure to conceive is that they cannot control everything about the process. Many women are used to working really hard toward a goal, often researching it and taking the best possible path, following all of the steps and obtaining the desired object. Using birth control to prevent pregnancy perpetuates the belief that fertility is something you can control. Unfortunately, when it comes to baby-making, you can do everything right and still not conceive. This is infuriating.

The reality is that we have almost no control over many things in our lives. The sheer fact that we wake up every morning is a miracle; just ask someone who has lost a loved one unexpectedly. The same principle applies to trying to conceive. To increase your chances of conceiving and delivering a healthy baby, take a good prenatal vitamin, maintain a healthy weight, eat a variety of nutritious, colorful foods, get regular exercise, seek appropriate medical care—and of course, have well-timed and frequent intercourse. Unfortunately, none of this guarantees a healthy baby at the end. It's tough to acknowledge this. In fact, IVF has only about a 50 percent success rate in people with unexplained infertility (no medical diagnosis preventing conception). On the bright side, Sarah demonstrates that unexplained infertility can also resolve itself without explanation. Our bodies are dynamic, always changing.

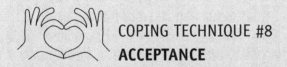

COPING TECHNIQUE #8
ACCEPTANCE

Perhaps the most classic example of acceptance is The Serenity Prayer: *God grant me the serenity to accept the things I cannot change, the courage to change the things I can, and the wisdom to know the difference.*

Recognizing what we can and cannot control is a stepping stone toward acceptance. When things don't go as we would like, we have a tendency to automatically rail against the situation. We fight it, reject it, or insist it must be different. This creates more stress, anger, and frustration. We need to learn that we can't change the situation, but we can change our response to it. Instead of having two problems—the situation and our bad feelings around it—we can learn acceptance, which softens the sting.

Acceptance is wholeheartedly receiving the situation. We may still feel anger, sadness, etc., at the situation but we are not fighting it. Acceptance is not about being passive. It's about being firm and brave. Acceptance of your difficulty is not tantamount to giving up. It also means you are still proactive in trying to change things or seek treatment.

Acceptance is wholeheartedly receiving the situation. We may still feel anger, sadness, etc., at the situation but we are not fighting it. Acceptance is not about being passive. It's about being firm and brave.

For example, if you are having trouble conceiving, then pursuing a fertility evaluation or intervention is not contrary to acceptance. It's the attitude you hold around the situation. Acceptance is the opposite of "grin and bear it." There is a huge difference between pursuing treatment with the understanding that this is your reality versus resenting it and hating that you need help. This may seem insincere if you are working toward acceptance but are not there yet. That's OK—most people aren't. Think about how you feel in your calm and hopeful moments, then let that be your guide. For example, you may have moments when you fear you won't ever be a mother and you may also have moments when you are OK that you're not pregnant. (Such as when someone is pouring the wine!) Tap into the positive moments.

Just like mindfulness, acceptance is a muscle that must be "built" in your brain, and the best way to do that is through meditation and mantra recitation. A guide for meditation is provided in Chapter 8. Instead of focusing on your breath, you can focus on a mantra. Some people like to start with their breath to center them. As described previously, you will need a good mindfulness practice to notice when you are rallying against the situation. Pick a mantra that speaks to you and try meditating five minutes a day on it. You can choose a short phrase from spiritual writings or poetry, or you could write your own short phrase. It is important that the mantra reflects your true feelings and also reflects acceptance of your situation. Below are some simple examples:

I whole-heartedly accept things as they are; I understand that they are temporary.

I am taking great care of myself, creating a safe place for my baby.

I will be a mother, I just don't know how or when yet.

People get pregnant, so will I. It is just taking longer than I like.

Throughout your day, repeat the mantra to yourself, especially when you start to sense stress rising. You can say it, chant it, sing it out loud, whisper it, or you can repeat it silently in your mind. Experiment and find out what's most effective for you.

We absolutely assure you that once your child arrives, you will need acceptance. You will need to accept that things that seemed routine before—haircuts, runs in the park, watching an entire TV show uninterrupted—may require elaborate scheduling. You will need it when there is a *poonami*. You will need it when you can only run one errand per day or else face total meltdown from a baby. Happy parenting requires acceptance, along with the other coping techniques we described in this book. Learn to give yourself that gift now.

Epilogue

Our book is a bit like Oprah on her "favorite things" episode: You get a baby, and you get a baby, and you get a baby! So what happens when the ending is not so sweet? Why weren't those stories included? We made a conscious decision to only include women who ended up with a child somehow, someway. There are people who make peace with not having children after a long struggle to conceive or a life that simply did not work out that way. We rejoice for their clarity and contentment. There are some of us, however, that would always feel something was missing. Sharon has seen this in her clinical practice and has felt this innately.

When we first planned the book, we imagined including at least one woman who had tried to conceive but never became a mother. In the end, we did not include any stories like this for two reasons. First, we do not think reading discouraging stories while you are trying to conceive would be helpful. Second, that subject merits its own book—in fact, excellent ones have been written. However, we have known women who gave up on trying to conceive because it became too stressful for them, rather than because it became biologically or financially unfeasible. We wrote this book to help women avoid letting stress derail their pursuit of motherhood.

We also could not present every possible path to parenthood. In our research, we have read about women conceiving with their eggs that they froze when they were younger, couples going to Israel for more aggressive fertility treatment, using surrogates in Southeast Asia who are more affordable than U.S. ones, adopting sibling sets, and foster parenting that leads to adoption.

We featured a variety of women, some who always felt the maternal pull, and others who were ambivalent until their child arrived. Some eagerly embraced ART while others knew that was not their path. One thing they all shared, though, was the sanctity of the experience. Conception, pregnancy, childbirth, and new motherhood have somehow been corrupted in our American society. They are the fodder for jokes and poorly written sitcom scenes. One reason we cringe at anyone saying "just" as in "just adopt" or "just do IVF," is that none of this is to be taken lightly. It is not like "just" going to the store for a quart of milk. It is an extreme privilege to parent, to be the keeper of a soul, the maker of a being. Whether you carry the child or not, you create the life. The women we interviewed understood that.

It is also not so easy. You only hear about it when it works. No one talks about the failed IVF cycles, the adoptions that fell through, and the perfectly timed sex that led nowhere. We wanted to give a space for that. We say multiple times in multiple ways that there is no secret formula to making a baby. Why some people conceive easily and others do not remains a mystery. The question, "What finally worked?" has no real answer. Fertility is dynamic and always changing.

Why did Emma have two miscarriages, then two easy conceptions? Why did it take Sharon and her husband three years when all the issues were "corrected" earlier on? We do not know. What we do know, what we have learned, we share below.

Emma's Story

As I write this, my children are seven and nine, and I cannot precisely remember what it was like to be preoccupied with my basal body temperature and whether my luteal phase was long enough. Intermittently during the past two years I would become wistful at the thought of a third baby. Once again, a dog rescued me from uncertainty—but this time with the opposite outcome. After we adopted a three-month-old springer spaniel named Jack, the ensuing sleepless nights, endless messes, and need to maintain vigilance against his self-destructive tendencies convinced me that I no longer have the patience for any more human babies. In Women's Bodies, Women's Wisdom, *Dr. Christiane Northrup talks about fertility as a metaphor and that we have many ways to express this fertility. At this point, I am content to no longer express my fertility by growing babies.*

Although the stories recorded here do not inform my life in a literal way, they have influenced me a lot. Ashley said, "It was frustrating, and at the same time, part of me just felt guilty for feeling sorry for myself, for us." After editing that passage I realized that I did that all the time too—having an emotion and then feeling that the emotion was wrong somehow—and that it was completely unhelpful. Since editing this story, I have tried to break that habit. I love Nicole's decision to follow her heart despite the apparent impracticality of it, and I feel like it has inspired bravery in me. (I also adore the fact that her sperm donor wanted to help her purely out of compassion.) Although you could describe Erin's experience as deciding not to decide, it can also be seen as letting go or letting things unfold naturally. Although I do not innately have Sarah's ability to accept things as they are, I think it is important to try to cultivate that attitude. Elizabeth talked about how she finally surrendered to the situation, and that is when things finally shifted.

Trying to tell other women's stories felt really weighty, and I am not sure I would do it again, but I really value the things I have learned from the process, which go way beyond sperm counts and hormone levels. These core practices—being mindful of thoughts and feelings, accepting what is, and even surrendering and opening to it—are what I aspire to bring to motherhood and all facets of my life.

Sharon's Story

I was always really open about our journey. In part because I find it cathartic to tell my story and to connect to others, in part because I always knew there would be a happy ending. People periodically ask me what finally worked. I answer based on their motivation. It is sacred stuff, not to be the subject of vapid chatter. As a Buddhist, I know that our karma finally ripened. Karma is cause and effect. Everything we experience is an effect of a cause created in this or a past life. Struggles are not punishment, they are simply negative karma ripening. They are impermanent. Joy is a manifestation of positive karma. However, it too is temporary. Nothing brings me greater joy than being with my daughter—except when I really need a minute to myself.

Intellectually, I understood this throughout our journey. Sometimes I was actually able to feel it and that brought great calm. The thing is, even now with my life as perfect as can be, the struggle persists. Will my beautiful baby girl grow to be strong and healthy? Will my husband and I continue to enjoy good health? Life changes in an instant.

After our daughter was born, I quit my job and stayed home full time. I loved it. I truly loved it. My world became so small and full. Mondays were hikes in the woods, Tuesdays story hour, and so on. My husband would come home and I would have a beautiful dinner made. The year ended with a decadent three-week stay on a remote Bahamian island. It was there that we learned that my sister-in-law had stage 3 breast cancer. She's not much older than me. Her girls are almost grown, but need her as much as mine needs me. We returned home.

I started a new job and we enrolled our daughter in play school. As I was driving to get her on her second day, my brother-in-law called to say that paramedics were attending to my father-in-law. He called back a few minutes later to say his father had passed. We were stunned. We moved through winter recalibrating, counting the blessings of our little trio amongst the fragility of our larger family. I continued to live in love. Focusing on what brought joy.

Meanwhile, my husband, who had been ambivalent about children before we got married, became baby crazy. We decided to have my IUD removed. Even though it had taken us so long to conceive the first time, I always knew fertility was variable. I had no reason to believe we wouldn't conceive easily the second time. I also wanted to be thoughtful about the timing of a second child. I knew we couldn't handle babies too close in age. Three months later, our daughter weaned herself at sixteen months. A few months after that, we conceived our second daughter. She is as perfect as our first.

This is life. Perceived struggle intertwined with perceived joy.

Recommended Resources

Please check with your healthcare provider before following any recommendation, especially once pregnant.

Fertility and Conception

Women's Bodies, Women's Wisdom
By Christiane Northrup

This is a pioneering book in the field of mind-body medicine and women's health. It addresses much more than fertility issues, but the sections on fertility and healing are deep and rich. It includes an in-depth discussion of how to identify your fertile window. Northrup presents a mix of both Western and Eastern medicine and complementary approaches to health. We particularly appreciate her discussion of fertility as a metaphor—and how our fertility is much more than our body's capacity to grow babies.

Making Babies: A Proven 3-Month Program for Maximum Fertility
By Sami S. David and Jill Blakeway

This book combines the best of Western and Eastern medicine in a clear, enjoyable-to-read format. David was the first reproductive endocrinologist in New York to do IVF and Blakeway is an experienced acupuncturist. They explain their thoughts on why some women conceive easily and others need more help, while offering gentle lifestyle interventions that can boost your chances for both natural conception and success with artificial reproductive technology.

Taking Charge of Your Fertility: The Definitive Guide to Natural Birth Control, Pregnancy Achievement, and Reproductive Health
By Toni Weschler

This is the fertility awareness method (FAM) bible. No, we are not talking about the rhythm method. FAM is based on your individual body and menstrual cycle. Weschler explains how to use basal body temperature (your oral temperature upon waking), cervical mucus, and cervical position to determine when you are fertile and when you are not. (After you have your baby, this will be handy as birth control!). We believe every woman, trying to conceive or not, should read this book to learn more about the menstrual cycle.

WomanCode: Perfect Your Cycle, Amplify Your Fertility, Supercharge Your Sex Drive, and Become a Power Source
By Alisa Vitti

Who doesn't want to be a "power source"? Vitti, a holistic health coach who cured her own polycystic ovary syndrome through years of research, offers a fresh and dynamic approach to health. We have honestly never seen anything like this despite our combined six degrees in nursing and health/research-related fields. While we are being forthcoming, neither of us was actually able to follow her plan, but we did glean some good information from it and implemented that in our own lives. Vitti's plan is based on five principles: stabilize blood sugar, calm adrenal glands, improve elimination, match diet and activity to phases of your menstrual cycle, and reconnect with your feminine side.

Mental Health

Conquering Infertility: Dr. Alice Domar's Mind/Body Guide to Enhancing Fertility and Coping with Infertility
By Alice Domar

Domar possesses both academic expertise and great empathy in helping people address the emotional side of infertility. She was inspired to pursue this specialty from her own mother's journey to become a parent. This is not a "how to get pregnant" book. It is a "how to cope with the journey" book. This book is an invaluable part of that mission. Domar offers practical tips that anyone can incorporate into their life along with helpful information.

The Secret
By Rhonda Byrne

This was the groundbreaking reintroduction of the law of attraction in the twenty-first century. Some may find this flaky, but both Emma and Sharon have found it life changing. It is a collection of thoughts and vignettes on the subject by various thought leaders in the field. Sharon found the audiobook more enjoyable.

The Power
By Rhonda Byrne

This is the sequel to *The Secret*. It elaborates on the law of attraction and gives tons of examples of it in action. Like *The Secret*, Sharon found the audiobook to be the most enjoyable way of experiencing it, especially if you have a long commute.

therapists.psychologytoday.com
You can find a therapist using this website. Simply type in your city and it will generate a list. You can refine the search by selecting ones that take your insurance, specialize in fertility issues, or offer a particular style.

kadampa.org
This is the website for Kadampa Buddhism. You can find a center near you and learn how to meditate. People of all faiths are welcome. You do not need to be a Buddhist nor is there any expectation of conversion.

headspace.com
This website offers an app to learn how to meditate. Think of it as your "personal trainer" for a clearer mind.

calm.com
This website also offers an app for guided meditations.

nurtured-well.com
This is the website for Sharon's mental health practice for readers in the Baltimore area.

Older Mom Memoirs and Blogs

The Doctor and the Stork: A Memoir of Modern Medical Babymaking
By K.K. Goldberg

This hilarious memoir recounts, week by week, the author's IVF-to-twin-birth story. This is the book for anyone contemplating IVF. (Spoiler alert: IVF is the easy part.) Goldberg places more faith in wheatgrass than modern medicine but eventually relents to IVF after four years of trying to conceive.

In an interview with Sharon, Goldberg explained why she wrote this book:

> *"I never intended to write about infertility, twins, or pregnancy—in my pre-kid life, I would have categorized this as 'over sharing.' However, throughout IVF, and then while carrying twins, I found myself taking detailed notes as an effective yet private way to vent. Some of my feelings*

seemed so extreme and so negative I couldn't share them elsewhere. When I looked back at those journals, I realized some of it was quite funny, if by accident, and I began to shape entries into the book. I wanted to craft something for other women going through the experience of carrying twins, or any pregnancy after IVF. There's so much written for and about 'natural' baby making—but so many of us go the opposite route."

Inconceivable: A Woman's Triumph Over Despair and Statistics
By Julia Indichova

Indichova recounts her struggle conceiving her second child in this poetically written memoir. Her journey starts outward and ends inward. At the age of 42 (after conceiving her daughter on the first try at age 40), she is told her eggs are too old and to start investigating donor eggs, surrogates, or adoption. Instead, she embarks on a two-year mission that includes everything from New York's best fertility specialists to "mystic" healers. In the process, she learns to rely on her intuition and transforms herself into a "fertile life force." She aims to inspire and educate others, "Just enough to realize the answers they come up with on their own could be as significant as the answers of the experts..."

beyondtheeggtimer.com
psychologytoday.com/blog/beyond-the-egg-timer
We would be remiss in not sharing our own blogs!

achildafter40.com
This website offers blogs, articles, inspirational stories, and a support community for those pursuing motherhood over 40.

Pregnancy and Parenting

The Essential Homebirth Guide: For Families Planning or Considering Birthing at Home
By Jane E. Drichta and Jodilyn Owen

An empowering, easy-to-read book written to help women un-cover how and where to birth and to advocate for the kind of care that is best for them. With a focus on families, these compassion-ate professional midwives describe the best way to experience a homebirth and also cover prenatal care, medical testing, vaginal birth after cesareans, common pregnancy-related issues, and special circumstances for moms no matter where they choose to birth. A foreword by Dr. Christiane Northrup, author of *Women's Bodies, Women's Wisdom*, encourages mothers to access their innate birthing wisdom.

Your Pregnancy and Childbirth, Month to Month by American College of Obstetrics and Gynecology
This is the authoritative guide, no nonsense and trusted by mid-wives and obstetricians.

The Science of Mom: A Research-Based Guide to Your Baby's First Year
By Alice Callahan

How long after birth should you cut the umbilical cord? Will bed sharing lead to sudden infant death syndrome? When can I start solids? What's the deal with peanuts? Those and a billion other questions are answered clearly in this book. Callahan, a nutri-tional biologist who studied fetal metabolism before becoming a mom, not only explores the science behind some hot parenting topics but more importantly, teaches the reader how to think like a scientist. This will be very important to you as you are bom-barded with information. News agencies are often quick to report on a new study but don't always interpret the data holistically.

Callahan arms you with basic statistical knowledge to navigate the often overwhelming world of "official medical recommendations." She also makes clear just how gray most areas are. This is actually reassuring, because you will quickly find that there are multiple ways of doing everything and your child will run you through the paces.

Expecting Better: Why the Conventional Pregnancy Wisdom Is Wrong—and What You Really Need to Know
By Emily Oster

Oster has a PhD in economics, not public health or nursing; however, she uses her research skills to investigate common pregnancy misconceptions like whether or not you can actually eat tuna and the all-important question: Is coffee safe? This book is for the rational woman who prefers to make decisions based on actual statistics not wives' tales. It is also very reassuring, especially if you accidentally keep eating things that are on the "no-no" list.

Other

Decisive
By Chip and Dan Heath

This book offers a fresh approach to decision-making. So long pro-and-con lists. The Heath brothers use research and psychological perspectives to give the reader validated techniques to reaching decisions.

RESOLVE.org
This is the National Infertility Association's website. They offer advocacy, information, and support.

Endnotes

1   Barry Schwartz. "The Paradox of Choice." Filmed July 2005 at TEDGlobal 2005. Video, 19:34. https://www.ted.com/talks/barry_schwartz_on_the_paradox_of_choice.

2   Tiffany Han. "Lisa Solomon on Being an Artist," March 22, 2016, in *Raise Your Hand Say Yes with Tiffany Han*, MP3 audio, 1:22:26, https://www.tiffanyhan.com/blog/lisasolomon.

3   Chip Heath and Dan Heath. *Decisive: How to Make Better Choice in Life and Work*. (New York: Crown Business, New York, 2013).

4   Sharon Praissman and Emma Williams. "Sperm vs. Gravity: True or False: Elevating Hips After Sex Improves the Chance of Pregnancy?" Beyond the Egg Timer (blog), *Psychology Today*. February 27, 2014. https://www.psychologytoday.com/blog/beyond-the-egg-timer/201402/sperm-vs-gravity.

5   Howard Markman and Scott M. Stanley. *Fighting for Your Marriage: A Deluxe Revised Edition of the Classic Best-seller for Enhancing Marriage and Preventing Divorce, 3rd Edition*, (Jossey-Bass, 2010).

6   Hannah Caradonna. "I Don't Want to Have Kids If It Changes My Life Too Much," Beyond the Egg Timer (blog), *Psychology Today*. March 27, 2014. https://www.psychologytoday.com/blog/beyond-the-egg-timer/201403/i-don-t-want-kids-if-it-changes-my-life-too-much.

7   Brady E. Hamilton et al., "Births: Final Data for 2014," *National Vital Statistics Reports*, Volume 64, Number 12. U.S. Department of Health and Human Services, December 2015. http://www.cdc.gov/nchs/data/nvsr/nvsr64/nvsr64_12.pdf.

8   Man Yee Mallory Leung, Fane Groes, and Raul Santaeulalia-Llopis, (2016) "The Relationship between Age at First Birth and Mother's Lifetime Earnings: Evidence from Danish Data." *PLoS ONE 11*, no. 1 (January 22, 2016).

9   United States Census Bureau. "Child Care Costs on the Upswing, Census Bureau Reports" Press release no. CB13-62 (April 3, 2013). https://www.census.gov/newsroom/press-releases/2013/cb13-62.html.

10 Erica Johnston, "How One Family Is Sending 13 Kids to College,

Living Debt Free — and Still Plans to Retire Early," *Washington Post*, August 11, 2016. https://www.washingtonpost.com/lifestyle/magazine/13-kids-13-college-educations-not-rich-retiring-early/2016/08/08/3abe7cec-38b4-11e6-a254-2b336e293a3c_story.html.

[11] Lynne Twist and Teresa Baker. *The Soul of Money: Reclaiming the Wealth of Our Inner Resources*. (New York: W. W. Norton & Company, 2006).

[12] Ben Hewitt. *Saved: How I Quit Worrying about Money and Became the Richest Guy in the World*, (New York: Rodale, 2013).

[13] Ann-Marie Slaughter, "Why Women Still Can't Have It All", *The Atlantic* (July/Aug 2012). https://www.theatlantic.com/magazine/archive/2012/07/why-women-still-cant-have-it-all/309020/.

[14] "How Long Does It Usually Take to Get Pregnant?" NHS in England, last reviewed November 21, 2015. http://www.nhs.uk/chq/Pages/2295.aspx?CategoryID=54.

[15] Christian Gnoth, D.Godehardt, E.Godehardt, P.Frank-Herrmann and G.Freundl, "Definition and Prevalence of Subfertility and Infertility," *Human Reproduction*, volume 20, no. 5 (May 2005): 1144–1147.

[16] David B. Dunson, Donna D. Baird, and Bernardo Colombo, "Increased Infertility With Age in Men and Women," *Obstetrics & Gynecology* 130, no. 1 (January 2004): 51–56.

[17] P. Cavoretto , M. Candiani1 V. Giorgione, A. Inversetti , M. M. Abu-Saba, F. Tiberio, C. Sigismondi, and A. Farina, "Risk of Spontaneous Preterm Birth in Singleton Pregnancies Conceived after IVF/ICSI Treatment: Meta-Analysis of Cohort Studies," *Ultrasound in Obstetrics & Gynecology* 51, no. 1 (January 2018): 43–53.

[18] Ranjith Ramasamy, Koji Chiba, Peter Butler, and Dolores J. Lamb, "Male Biological Clock: A Critical Analysis of Advanced Paternal Age," *Fertility and Sterility* 103, no. 6 (June 2015): 1402–1406, doi: 10.1016/j.fertnstert.2015.03.011.

[19] Rakesh Sharma, Ashok Agarwal, Vikram K Rohra, Mourad Assidi, Muhammad Abu-Elmagd and Rola F Turki, "Effects of Increased Paternal Age on Sperm Quality, Reproductive Outcome and Associated Epigenetic Risks to Offspring," *Reproductive Biology and Endocrinology* 13, no.35 (April 19, 2015), doi: 10.1186/s12958-015-0028-x.

[20] Christiane Northrup, *Women's Bodies, Women's Wisdom (Revised Edition): Creating Physical and Emotional Health and Healing* (New York: Bantam, 2010).

[21] Cesar Mora-Esteves and David Shin, "Nutrient Supplementation:

Improving Male Fertility Fourfold," *Seminars in Reproductive Medicine* 31, no. 4 (2013): 293–300.

22 Elsje Oostingh, Régine Steegers-Theunissen, Jeanne de Vries, Joop Laven, and Maria Koster, "Strong adherence to a healthy dietary pattern is associated with better semen quality, especially in men with poor semen quality," *Fertility and Sterility* 107, no. 4 (April 2017): 916–923. e2. doi: 10.1016/j.fertnstert.2017.02.103. Epub 2017 Mar 11.

23 Raj Rai and Lesley Regan, "Recurrent miscarriage" *Lancet* 368, no. 9535 (2006): 601–611.

24 Mark Dempsey, Karen Flood, Naomi Burke, Patricia Fletcher, Colin Kirkham, Michael Geary, and Fergal D. Malone, "Perinatal outcomes of women with a prior history of unexplained recurrent miscarriage," *The Journal of Maternal-Fetal & Neonatal Medicine* 28, no. 5 (2015): 522–5. http://dx.doi.org/10.3109/14767058.2014.923394.

25 Jaana Männistö, Aini Bloigu, Maarit Mentula, Mika Gissler, Mika Gissler, Oskari Heikinheimo, and Maarit Niinimäki. "Interpregnancy Interval After Termination of Pregnancy and the Risks of Adverse Outcomes in Subsequent Birth," *Obstetrics & Gynecology* 129, no. 2 (Feb 2017): 347–354. doi: 10.1097/AOG.0000000000001836.

26 A.M. Brkovuh and W.A. Fisher, Psychological distress and infertility: forty years of research, *Journal of Psychosomatic Obstetrics & Gynecology* 19, 4 (1998): 218–228.

27 Alice D. Domar, Diane Clapp, Ellen Slawsby, Bruce Kessel, E. John Orav, and Melissa Freizinger, "The impact of group psychological interventions on distress in infertile women," *Health Psychology* 19, no. 6, (2000): 568–575.

28 Alice D. Domar, Kristin L. Rooney, Benjamin Wiegand., E. John Orav, Michael M. Alper, Brian M. Berger, and Janeta Nikolovski, "Impact of a group mind/body intervention on pregnancy rates in IVF patients, " *Fertility and Sterility* 95 (June 2011): 2269–2273.

29 Cynthia Bourgeault, *The Wisdom Way of Knowing: Reclaiming an Ancient Tradition to Awaken the Heart* (San Francisco, CA: Jossey-Bass, 2003).

30 Tosha Silver, *Outrageous Openness: Letting the Divine Take the Lead.* (New York: Atria Books, 2014).

31 Jon Kabat-Zinn, J. *Full Catastrophe Living: Using the Wisdom of your Body and Mind to Face Stress, Pain, and Illness.* (New York: Bantam Dell, 2009).

32 Sharon Praissman and Emma Williams, "The Paradox of Procreation: When couples are trying to conceive, does it reduce their

sexual satisfaction?" Beyond the Egg Timer (blog), PsychologyToday, (Nov 28, 2013) https://www.psychologytoday.com/blog/beyond-the-egg-timer/201311/the-paradox-procreation.

33 Kenneth J. Rothman, Lauren A. Wise, Henrik T. Sørensen, Anders H. Riis, Ellen M. Mikkelsen, and Elizabeth E. Hatch, "Volational determinants and age-related decline in fecundabiliy: a general population cohort study in Denmark," *Fertility and Sterility* 99, no. 7 (2013): 1958-1964. http://dx.doi.org/10.1016/j.fertnstert.2013.02.040.

34 Jan L. Shifren, Brigitta U. Monz, Patricia A. Russo, et al. "Sexual Problems and Distress in United States Women," *Obstetrics & Gynecology* 112, no. 5 (2008): 970–978.

35 Rothman, et al. "Volitional determinants and age-related decline in fecundability: a general population prospective cohort study in Denmark."

36 Emily Evans-Hoeker, David A. Pritchard, D. Leann Long, Amy H. Herring, Joseph B. Stanford, and Anne Z. Steiner, "Cervical mucus monitoring prevalence and associated fecundability in women trying to conceive," *Fertility and Sterility* 100, no. 4 (Oct 2013):1033–1038. e1. doi: 10.1016/j.fertnstert.2013.06.002. Epub 2013 Jul 11.

37 Janet E. Robinson and Jayne E. Ellis, "Mistiming of Intercourse as a Primary Cause of Failure to Conceive: Results of a Survey on Use of a Home-Use Fertility Monitor," *Current Medical Research & Opinion* 23, no. 2, (Feb 2007): 301–6.

38 Allen J. Wilcox, Clarice R. Weinberg, and Donna D. Baird, "Timing of Sexual Intercourse in Relation to Ovulation—Effects on the Probability of Conception, Survival of the Pregnancy, and Sex of the Baby," *New England Journal of Medicine*, no. 333 (December 7, 1995): 1517–1521. doi: 10.1056/NEJM199512073332301.

39 Allen J. Wilcox, David Dunson, and Donna D. Baird. "The Timing of the 'Fertile Window' in the Menstrual Cycle: Day Specific Estimates from a Prospective Study," *BMJ* 321 (November 2000): 1259–62. http://dx.doi.org/10.1136/bmj.321.7271.1259.

40 Allen J. Wilcox. *Fertility and Pregnancy: An Epidemiologic Perspective.* (NewYork: Oxford University Press, 2010).

41 Allen J. Wilcox, Donna D. Baird, and David Dunson, "On the Frequency of Intercourse around Ovulation: Evidence for Biological Influences," *Human Reproduction* 19, no. 7 (July 2004): 1539–43.

42 Northrup, *Women's Bodies, Women's Wisdom.*

43 Wilcox, "On the Frequency of Intercourse around Ovulation: Evidence for Biological Influences."

Acknowledgments

Hannah Caradonna formed the knitting group that started our friendship, and she made important contributions to our book. Our friends Elaina Agee, Rachel Haws, and Nina Solomon were early reviewers with invaluable suggestions. The fabulous Judie Harvey was our editor extraordinaire. She kindly introduced us to Jodilyn Owen, whose expert opinion and generosity made this project complete. Thank you to Dr. Christiane Northrup for lighting the way and sharing the flame.

We were lucky that Silke Stein decided to enter our book cover design contest on 99designs.com. Nora Gaskin Esthimer of Lystra Books and Kelly Prelipp Lojk of Lojk Design were a dream for first time authors like us.

Most importantly, we appreciate all of the daring women who shared their stories in this book. You are most powerful when you are most vulnerable. Your words will inspire, touch, heal, and soothe countless women. For that there is no thanks great enough.

THANKS FROM EMMA
Thank you to Leonie, Lila, and Mark for loving me whether or not I accomplish much of anything. My sister and friends always encourage my myriad creative projects. I never would have completed this book without the support of my parents and in-laws, which included lots of free childcare.

THANKS FROM SHARON
Thanks to Bryan, for loving me and conspiring in a lifetime of "dreaming and scheming"; my mother and number one fan who knows the world is full of everyday miracles and is not ashamed to show it; Starr Whitney, wherever you are, for not accepting mediocracy from me; my family and friends for believing I was capable of this.

ABOUT THE AUTHORS

Emma Williams lives in western Maryland with her husband, two children, and two dogs. She works for Jhpiego, specializing in public health evaluation and research.

Sharon Praissman Fisher is dually board certified as an adult (medical) and psychiatric mental health nurse practitioner. She is also a wife, mother, Buddhist lay teacher, and Chesapeake Bay sailor. She is passionate about helping women through all stages of their lives and does so though her private practice, Nurtured Well, LLC, in Baltimore, Maryland.

Printed in Great Britain
by Amazon

31938907R00096